New York Review Series

GRADE 6
MATHEMATICS

 Glencoe

Image Credits: (l) Getty Images, (2) Getty Images, (3) CORBIS, (4) Comstock Images

The *McGraw·Hill* Companies

 Glencoe

Send all inquiries to:
Glencoe/McGraw-Hill
8787 Orion Place
Columbus, OH 43240-4027

ISBN: 978-0-07-888547-1
MHID: 0-07-888547-7

New York Review Series, Grade 6 Mathematics SE

Printed in the United States of America.

2 3 4 5 6 7 8 9 10 047 10 09 08

Contents

Unit 1: Review of Grade 5 Performance Indicators (Post-March)

Chapter 1: Grade 5 Algebra

Chapter 2: Grade 5 Geometry

Chapter 3: Grade 5 Statistics and Probability

Unit 2: Grade 6 Performance Indicators (Pre-March)

Chapter 4: Grade 6 Number Sense and Operations

Chapter 5: More Grade 6 Number Sense and Operations

Chapter 8: Grade 6 Measurement

Chapter 9: Grade 6 Statistics and Probability

How to Master the New York Test

What is the New York Test?

In March, you will be taking the New York State Test in Mathematics for Grade 6. The test covers the topics and skills that you will be learning at school this year from September to March. It also covers the topics you were taught last spring in your fifth-grade math class.

Your performance on the test will show how well you have learned the material that is required of all sixth-grade students in the state. It can also help you and your teacher identify which areas and skills you are strong in, and which you may need to focus on and develop.

There are three types of questions that you will see on the test:
- Multiple Choice
- Short Response
- Extended Response

For multiple-choice questions, you will need to choose the correct answer to a problem from four given choices. Short- and extended-response questions, however, ask you to solve a problem and write your own answer. You may also need to show your work by writing out each step in your calculations, drawing a picture, or describing in words how you solved the problem.

The test is divided into three sessions that are stretched out over two days. Here is a breakdown of the type and number of questions that are included in each test session.

	Session	Multiple Choice	Short Response	Extended Response	Total Questions	Time
Day 1	1	25	—	—	25	45 min
Day 2	2	—	6	4	10	60 min
	Total	25	6	4	35	105 min

Knowing what kinds of questions to expect on a test can help you to prepare and do your best. The following examples demonstrate the three types of questions you will see on the New York State Test, and some tips that you can use to solve each.

Multiple-Choice Questions

All of the questions in Session 1 are multiple choice. For these questions, you will be asked to choose the correct answer to a problem from four given choices. Calculators are NOT allowed during this part of the test.

Follow these steps to help you answer this type of question:

1. **Read the question carefully and look over any graphic that may be included.**
2. **Read all the answer choices and cross out any that you know are wrong.**
3. **Solve the problem.**
4. **Check your answer.**
5. **Make sure you clearly mark that correct answer on your scorecard.**

EXAMPLE

1 Rick ran $\frac{2}{4}$ of a mile. David ran $\frac{1}{5}$ of a mile. How far did they run altogether?

 A $\frac{13}{20}$ of a mile

 B $\frac{3}{20}$ of a mile

 C $\frac{1}{3}$ of a mile

 D $\frac{7}{10}$ of a mile

You need to find how far they ran altogether. To solve the problem, you can add $\frac{2}{4}$ and $\frac{1}{5}$.

Now look at the answer choices. You know that both answers B and C are incorrect because they are too small. After eliminating these choices, the only possible answers are A and D.

Use scrap paper to solve the problem: $\frac{2}{4} + \frac{1}{5} = \frac{14}{20} = \frac{7}{10}$, so the correct answer is D, $\frac{7}{10}$ of a mile.

Check your answer by subtracting: $\frac{7}{10} - \frac{1}{5} = \frac{5}{10} = \frac{1}{2}$, or $\frac{2}{4}$, so your answer is correct. On your scorecard, fill in the circle for answer D.

Tips
- If you do not understand the question or cannot eliminate any of the answer choices, move on to the next question. You can come back to this question when you finish the rest of the questions in the section.
- If you can eliminate two of the answer choices but cannot solve the problem, then make your best guess. No points will be taken off your score for a wrong answer, and you have a good chance of guessing correctly!

Short-Response and Extended-Response Questions

All of the questions in Session 2 will be short or extended response. These questions will ask you to solve a problem and write your own answer on the line(s) provided. You may also need to show your work by writing down each step in the problem, drawing a picture, completing a chart, or explaining in words how you found the answer.

The only difference between short- and extended-response questions is that extended-response questions have two or more parts. Calculators ARE allowed during this part of the test.

Follow these steps to help you answer these types of questions:

1. Read the question carefully and look over any graphic that may be included.
2. Pick the best method for solving the problem.
3. Solve the problem.
4. Check the final answer and write it on the given line(s) or space.
5. Make sure that you show your work and that you have answered each part of the question.

SHORT–RESPONSE EXAMPLE

1 Tommy digs a circle around a tree in his yard like the one shown below. What is the circumference of the circle? Use the formula $C = 2\pi r$. Leave your answer in terms of π.

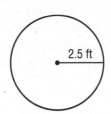

2.5 ft

Show your work.

Answer _____ feet

For this question, you are given a diagram to use. The diagram gives you the radius of the circle. To solve the problem, you replace the *r* in the formula with the length of the radius and multiply.

You can use your calculator to multiply. However, you must write out the steps in the given space to show how you found your answer. It is also a good idea to label your work, as shown.

Show your work.

Circumference of a circle
⇓
$2 \times \pi \times 2.5 = 5\pi$

Is the circumference of the circle 5π feet? The diagram shows the radius is 2.5 feet. You can check your answer by adding 2.5 and 2.5.

$$\text{radius} + \text{radius} = 2.5 + 2.5 = 5.0 \text{ or } 5$$
$$\text{circumference} = \pi \times 5 = 5\pi$$

Your answer is correct, so write 5π on the line labeled *Answer*. Notice that the units are already written for you.

The same question could also be used as the first part, or *Part A*, of an extended response question. In this case, the second part of the extended response question would be labeled *Part B*, as below. The example below shows how you could answer this part of the question.

EXTENDED RESPONSE EXAMPLE

Part B

If you double the radius, what will the circumference be? Explain how you would find the answer on the lines below.

The diagram shows that the radius is 2.5 feet. If I double the radius,

then I'll multiply 2 × 2.5. Since 2 × 2.5 = 5, I will replace the r in the

formula for the circumference with 5. The circumference = 2 × π × 5

= 10π. If the radius is doubled, the circumference is 10π feet.

Tip

- Even if you do not get the correct final answer, you may be given points for the work you have done. For this reason, it is VERY important that you write or draw as neatly as possible when showing your work.

Test-Taking Tips

When you take any test, there are some things that you should always do:

1. Try to get a full night's sleep before the test, so you are well rested.
2. Read the directions carefully. If you do not understand what you are supposed to do, ask your teacher to explain before the test begins.
3. Read each question carefully.
4. Manage your time for each section. If you are not sure how to solve a problem, skip it. Then go back to it once you have finished the other problems in the section.
5. Check your answer for each problem.

How to Use This Book

This book will help you review and develop the math skills you need to succeed on the New York State Test in Mathematics for Grade 6. The extra practice that you will gain from going over the solved examples and doing the problems will also help you to do better in your schoolwork throughout the year.

Unit 1 is a review of the fifth-grade topics that may be included on the test. Unit 2 includes all of the sixth-grade material that you will be expected to know. However, the lessons are written so that you can review them in any order. Using the table of contents, you can easily find the lessons that focus on the topics you need the most help with.

Every lesson has the following features:

- A list of skills or performance indicators, including the process skills that you will need to apply to the problems.
- Any vocabulary and definitions that you will need to know for the lesson.
- Basic facts and background information on the topic, to help you get up to speed.
- Two or three example problems, solved step-by-step.
- *Understanding the Solution:* Explanations of the answers for each solved example or how to check your answer.
- *Try It:* Example problems that you can solve on your own using the same methods.
- *Exercises:* Multiple-choice, short-response, and extended-response practice questions that are like the questions you may find on the test.

Special *Problem-Solving Lessons* are also included in each chapter. These shorter lessons help you to develop and use different methods for solving problems.

Each chapter and unit in the book is also followed by a sample practice test. These tests provide extra practice in the different ways that each topic may be tested.

The next page contains a list of formulas and other information that you will need to know and use to solve problems. Use this sheet to help you identify and review important concepts.

Mathematics Reference Sheet—Grade 6

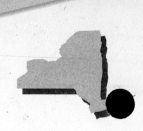

Conversions

Temperature Conversion

$$C = \frac{5}{9} \times (F - 32)$$

$$F = \left(\frac{9}{5} \times C\right) + 32$$

Measurement Conversion

1 pint (pt) = 2 cups
1 quart (qt) = 2 pints
1 gallon (gal) = 4 quarts

1 liter (L) = 1,000 milliliters
1 milliliter (mL) = 0.001 liter

Formulas

Distance formula $\qquad\qquad d = r \times t$
Simple interest formula $\qquad I = p \times r \times t$

Perimeter of a rectangle
$P = 2\ell + 2w$

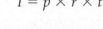

Perimeter of a square
$P = 4s$

Area of a rectangle
$A = \ell \times w$

Area of a square
$A = s^2$

Area of a parallelogram
$A = b \times h$

Area of a rhombus
$A = b \times h$

Area of a triangle
$A = \frac{1}{2} \times b \times h$

Area of a trapezoid
$A = \frac{1}{2}(b_1 + b_2)\, h$

Area of a circle
$A = \pi r^2$

Volume of a rectangular prism
$V = \ell wh$

Circumference of a circle
$C = \pi d$

Area of a sector of a circle
$A = \dfrac{\text{Central angle}}{360} \times \pi r^2$

Writing and Evaluating Algebraic Expressions

New York Performance Indicators

5.A.2 Translate simple verbal expressions into algebraic expressions

5.A.3 Substitute assigned values into variable expressions and evaluate using order of operations

6.PS.7 Represent problem situations verbally, numerically, algebraically, and/or graphically

6.PS.8 Select an appropriate representation of a problem

VOCABULARY

A **variable** is a letter or symbol used to represent an unknown quantity.

An **algebraic expression** is an expression that contains operations with variables and numbers.

To **evaluate** an algebraic expression means to find the value of the expression.

REVIEW

Understanding Algebraic Expressions

An expression can be written as a verbal expression and as an algebraic expression. For example, the verbal expression "the sum of three and a number" translates to the algebraic expression written below.

$$3 + n$$

You can evaluate an expression by replacing the variable with a numerical value. Let $n = 7$, then replace n with 7 and perform the operation.

$$3 + n = 3 + 7$$
$$= 10$$

Applying Algebraic Expressions

You have a coupon for d dollars off a new pair of tennis shoes. Write an expression for the cost of a $27 pair of tennis shoes with the coupon. Then find the cost of the tennis shoes if the value of the coupon is $5.

Let d represent the value of the coupon.

$$27 - d$$

To find the cost of the tennis shoes with the coupon, replace d with 5.

$$27 - d = 27 - 5$$
$$= 22$$

The cost of the tennis shoes with the coupon is $22.

Translating Verbal Expressions

You can translate verbal expressions into algebraic expressions by replacing the words with related numbers and operations.

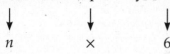

EXAMPLE 1

Write an algebraic expression for the verbal expression "a number multiplied by six."

You can solve this problem by translating the words into numbers, variables, and operations. Translate each part of the verbal expression into a number, variable, or operation.

[a number] [multiplied by] [six]

$$n \qquad \times \qquad 6$$

This can also be written as $6n$.

▶ **Understanding the Solution** The words *a number* can be represented by a variable such as n. The words *multiplied by* mean to multiply, so use a multiplication sign. For the word *six* write the number 6.

TRY IT!

Write an algebraic expression for the verbal expression "seventeen less than a number."

Evaluating an Expression

An algebraic expression can be evaluated by replacing the variable with a given number or value.

EXAMPLE 2

Evaluate $t \div 7$ for $t = 21$.

You can solve this problem by replacing the variable with the given number.
Replace t with 21. $\quad t \div 7$
$$21 \div 7$$

Perform the operation.

$$21 \div 7 = 3$$

▶ **Understanding the Solution** Replace the variable t with the number 21. Then perform the division.

TRY IT!

Evaluate $v + 2$ if $v = 27$.

EXAMPLE 3

Jamie can assemble 9 back-to-school packets in one hour. The expression $9h$ represents the number of packets she can assemble in h hours. How many packets can Jamie assemble in 8 hours?

You can solve this problem by evaluating the expression.
Evaluate the expression $9h$ for $h = 8$.

Replace h with 8. $9h$
                             $9(8)$

Perform the operation.

$$9(8) = 72$$

▶ **Understanding the Solution**   The expression $9h$ represents the number of back to school packets Jamie can assemble in h hours. If Jamie assembles packets for 8 hours, she will assemble 72 packets.

TRY IT!

Steve earned $56 mowing lawns last week. The expression $56 \div m$ represents the amount of money he earned per lawn. If Steve mowed 7 lawns, how much money did he earn for mowing one lawn?

Exercises

SHORT RESPONSE

1 Tickets to the school play cost $9 per ticket. Write an algebraic expression to show the cost of x tickets. Then use that algebraic expression to find the total cost of tickets for 5 people.

Show your work.

$9 = per ticket$

$9xX = 9x5 = 45$

Answer ___45 = 5 people.___

2 Which algebraic expression represents the verbal expression "16 decreased by a number?"

- **A** $n - 16$
- **B** $16 - n$
- **C** $n + 16$
- **D** $16 + n$

$16 - n$

decreased

3 Which verbal expression represents the algebraic expression $2c$?

- **A** twice a number
- **B** a number divided by two
- **C** half a number
- **D** two more than a number

4 Which algebraic expression represents the verbal expression "the sum of a number and 23?"

- **A** $23 \div n$
- **B** $23 - n$
- **C** $n + 23$
- **D** $23n$

5 Evaluate the expression $45 \div t$ for $t = 5$.

- **A** 9
- **B** 40
- **C** 50
- **D** 225

6 Evaluate the expression $24 + k$ for $k = 6$.

- **A** 4
- **B** 18
- **C** 30
- **D** 144

7 Evaluate the expression $8m$ for $m = 7$.

- **A** 1
- **B** 15
- **C** 42
- **D** 56

8 Ben needs to buy folders for school. The folders are $0.25 each. If f represents the number of folders he needs to buy, which algebraic expression represents the cost of the folders?

- **A** $0.25 + f$
- **B** $0.25 - f$
- **C** $0.25f$
- **D** $0.25 \div f$

9 Mrs. Holly spent $24 buying new rulers for her sixth grade class. The expression $24 \div r$ represents the amount of money she spent per ruler. If Mrs. Holly bought 12 rulers, how much did each ruler cost?

- **A** $1.00
- **B** $1.50
- **C** $2.00
- **D** $2.50

EXTENDED RESPONSE

10 Mr. Hodges would like to put a fence around his square vegetable garden.

Part A

Write an algebraic expression for the perimeter of the garden. Indicate what the variable in the expression represents in your work.

Show your work.

Answer _____

Part B

If the length of one side of the square garden is 10 feet, what is the perimeter of the garden?

Show your work.

Answer _____

New York Performance Indicators

5.A.4 Solve simple one-step equations using basic whole-number facts

5.A.5 Solve and explain simple one-step equations using inverse operations involving whole numbers

6.PS.2 Understand that some ways of representing a problem are more efficient than others

VOCABULARY

An **equation** is a mathematical statement with an equals sign, $=$, indicating that the left side of the equals sign has the same value as the right side.

A **solution** to an equation is a value that makes the equation true.

Inverse operations are operations that undo each other. Addition and subtraction are inverse operations. Multiplication and division are inverse operations.

REVIEW

Understanding Solving Equations

You solve one-step equations by finding the value of the variable that makes the equation true. One way to do this is use basic facts.

$$3 + x = 7$$

Think to yourself, what value of x will make the equation true?

$$3 + 4 = 7$$
$$x = 4$$

You can also solve equations using inverse operations.

$$x - 9 = 2$$

Add 9 to both sides of the equation to undo the subtraction of 9 on the left side.

$$
\begin{array}{r}
x - 9 = 2 \\
+\,9 = +9 \\
\hline
x = 11
\end{array}
$$

To undo subtraction, you add. To undo addition, you subtract. To undo multiplication, you divide. To undo division, you multiply.

Applying Solving Equations

A basketball team scored 29 points in the first half of the game. Seventeen points were scored in the second quarter of the game. The equation that represents this situation is $p + 17 = 29$, where p is the number of points scored in the first quarter of the game. Solve the equation to find the number of points scored in the first quarter of the game.

$$
\begin{array}{r}
p + 17 = 29 \\
-\,17 = -17 \\
\hline
p = 12 \text{ points}
\end{array}
$$

Twelve points were scored in the first quarter of the game.

Solving Equations Using Mental Math

One-step equations can often be solved using mental math. Simply think about what value of the variable will make the equation true.

EXAMPLE 1

Solve the equation $2y = 12$.

You can solve this problem by asking yourself, "What number times two is twelve?"

$$2y = 12$$
$$2(6) = 12$$
$$y = 6$$

▷ **Understanding the Solution**   Since two times six is twelve, $y = 6$.

TRY IT!

Solve the equation $j + 7 = 13$.

Solving Equations Using Inverse Operations

One-step equations can also be solved using inverse operations.

EXAMPLE 2

Solve the equation $\frac{g}{7} = 5$.

You can solve this problem by using multiplication to undo the division.

$$\frac{g}{7} = 5$$
$$7 \cdot \frac{g}{7} = 7 \cdot 5$$
$$g = 35$$

▷ **Understanding the Solution**   To undo the division by 7, you multiply each side of the equation by 7.

$$7 \cdot 5 = 35, \text{ so } g = 35.$$

TRY IT!

Solve the equation $t - 21 = 9$.

EXAMPLE 3

Jose's dog gained 4 pounds, so it now weighs 23 pounds. The equation that represents this situation is $d + 4 = 23$, where d is the weight of Jose's dog before it gained 4 pounds. Solve the equation to find how much Jose's dog weighed before it gained 4 pounds.

You can solve this problem using subtraction to undo the addition.

$$
\begin{array}{rcr}
d + 4 = & 23 \\
-\ 4 = & -\ 4 \\
\hline
d = & 19
\end{array}
$$

▶ **Understanding the Solution**   Jose's dog weighed 19 pounds before it gained 4 pounds.

TRY IT!

Sam is 6 inches taller than Jack. Jack is 61 inches tall. The equation that represents this situation is $s - 6 = 61$, where s is Sam's height. Solve the equation to find Sam's height.

Exercises

SHORT RESPONSE

1 Which method of solving a one-step equation, using mental math or using inverse operations, would you use to solve the equation $n + 2 = 6$? Explain why.

Show your work.

Answer _____

_____

2 Which is a solution to the equation
$5m = 40$?

A $m = 8$
B $m = 35$
C $m = 45$
D $m = 200$

3 Which is a solution to the equation
$r - 36 = 62$?

A $r = 18$
B $r = 26$
C $r = 98$
D $r = 102$

4 Maura has 5 more pets than her friend Francis. Francis has 3 pets. The equation that represents this situation is $m - 5 = 3$, where m is the number of pets that Maura has. Solve the equation. How many pets does Maura have?

A 1 pet
B 2 pets
C 8 pets
D 15 pets

5 Last night 127 people attended the school play. Tonight 203 people attended. The equation that represents this situation is $127 + n = 203$, where n is the increase in the number of people who attended the play. How many more people attended the play tonight?

A 73
B 76
C 330
D 406

6 Which operation can be used to solve the equation $\frac{x}{9} = 4$?

A add 9 to both sides of the equation
B subtract 9 from both sides of the equation
C divide both sides of the equation by 9
D multiply both sides of the equation by 9

7 Solve the following equation.
$13z = 65$.

A $z = 5$
B $z = 52$
C $z = 78$
D $z = 845$

8 Solve the following equation. $h + 9 = 54$

A 6
B 13
C 45
D 63

9 You buy 6 cinnamon rolls for $9.00. The equation that can be used to find the cost of each cinnamon roll is $6r = 9$. How much does each cinnamon roll cost?

A $1.00
B $1.25
C $1.50
D $1.75

8 Use the equation $x + 124 = 492$ to answer the following questions.

Part A

Describe how you could use inverse operations to solve the equation.

Show your work.

Answer _____

_____

Part B

Solve the equation.

Show your work.

Answer _____

Problem-Solving Strategy: Solving Word Problems

 New York Performance Indicators

6.PS.3 Interpret information correctly, identify the problem, and generate possible strategies and solutions

6.PS.17 Determine what information is needed to solve problems

6.PS.22 Discuss whether a solution is reasonable in the context of the original problem

6.PS.23 Verify results of a problem

How Do You Solve a Problem?

When solving word problems, it is important to have a plan. You can use the four-step plan below to help you solve word problems.

Four-Step Problem-Solving Plan

1. Read the problem. Identify what you know and what you need to find out. Determine what information is needed to solve the problem.
2. Make a plan. Choose a strategy to help you solve the problem.
3. Solve the problem. Use the strategy you chose to solve the problem.
4. Check your answer. Reread the problem and decide whether your answer is reasonable.

Problem: Samantha is thinking of two one-digit numbers. The sum of the two numbers is 14, and their product is 45. Find the numbers.

SOLUTION

What do you know?

There are two numbers.

Each are one-digit numbers.

The sum of the two numbers is 14.

The product of the two numbers is 45.

What do you need to find?

What are the two numbers?

Find the relationship

Choose a strategy to help you solve this problem. You can use trial and error to solve this problem.

Choose two one-digit numbers whose sum is 14.	$7 + 7 = 14$
Check to see if their product is 45.	$7 \times 7 = 49$

The product of 7 and 7 is not 45. So repeat the process and try two more numbers.

Choose two one-digit numbers whose sum is 14.	$6 + 8 = 14$
Check to see if their product is 45.	$6 \times 8 = 48$

The product of 6 and 8 is not 45, so try two more numbers.

> Choose two one-digit numbers whose sum is 14. $5 + 9 = 14$
> Check to see if their product is 45. $5 \times 9 = 45$

The sum of 5 and 9 is 14, and the product of 5 and 9 is 45. The two numbers that Samantha was thinking of were 5 and 9.

▶ **Understanding the Solution**   Reread the problem. You are looking for two one-digit numbers whose sum is 14 and whose product is 45.

$$5 + 9 = 14 \text{ and } 5 \times 9 = 45$$

The numbers 5 and 9 are reasonable answers.

SHORT RESPONSE

1   Ken worked 8 weeks during the summer as a lifeguard. He was able to save $336. He earned the same amount of money each week and did not spend any of the money he made working as a lifeguard. How much money did Ken make each week?

Show your work.

Answer _____

2   Wanda is in a bicycling club. During each meeting, they ride a certain number of miles on their bikes. The table below shows how many miles Wanda rode during the first four meetings. If the pattern continues, how many miles will she ride during the sixth meeting?

Day	1	2	3	4
Number of miles	2	4	6	8

Show your work.

Answer _____

MULTIPLE CHOICE

1 Which algebraic expression represents the verbal expression "three times a number?"

   A $3n$

   B $3 + n$

   C $3 - n$

   D $3 \div n$

2 Which verbal expression represents the algebraic expression $x + 10$?

   A a number times ten

   B ten less than a number

   C a number divided by ten

   D ten more than a number

3 Evaluate the expression $c - 26$ for $c = 33$.

   A 7

   B 13

   C 17

   D 59

4 Evaluate the expression $t \div 7$ for $t = 63$.

   A 70

   B 54

   C 9

   D 3

5 Which is a solution to the equation $3x = 36$?

   A $x = 6$

   B $x = 12$

   C $x = 39$

   D $x = 108$

6 Which operation can be used to solve the equation $b + 9 = 15$?

   A Add 9 to both sides of the equation.

   B Multiply both sides of the equation by 9.

   C Divide both sides of the equation by 9.

   D Subtract 9 from both sides of the equation.

7 Betsy buys 4 notebooks for $8.00. The equation that can be used to find the cost of each notebook is $4n = 8$. How much does each notebook cost?

   A $1.00

   B $2.00

   C $4.00

   D $8.00

8 Brianna is 12 years older than her brother Jake. Jake is 6 years old. The equation $b - 12 = 6$ can represent this situation, where b is Brianna's age. How old is Brianna?

   A 2

   B 6

   C 12

   D 18

9 Mrs. Smith sells cookies for $2 per cookie.

Part A
Write an algebraic expression to show the cost of *x* cookies.
Show your work.

Answer _____

Part B
Find the total cost for 12 cookies.
Show your work.

Answer _____

10 Laura is thinking of two one-digit numbers whose sum is 11 and whose product is 18.

Part A
Find the two numbers.
Show your work.

Answer _____

Part B
After you have solved the problem, what should you do?

Answer _____

_____

LESSON 2.1 Graphing Coordinate Pairs

New York Performance Indicators

5.G.12 Identify and plot points in the first quadrant

6.PS.7 Represent problem situations verbally, numerically, algebraically, and/or graphically

VOCABULARY

A **coordinate plane** is formed when two number lines (called axes) intersect at right angles at their zero points; also called the coordinate system.

An **ordered pair** is a pair of numbers that are the coordinates of a point in a coordinate plane in this order (horizontal coordinate, vertical coordinate).

The **origin** is the point (0, 0) on a coordinate plane where the vertical axis meets the horizontal axis.

The **x-axis** is the horizontal axis in a coordinate plane. The **x-coordinate** is the first number of an ordered pair. It indicates how far to the left or right of the y-axis the corresponding point is.

The **y-axis** is the vertical axis in a coordinate plane. The **y-coordinate** is the second number of an ordered pair. It indicates how far above or below the x-axis the corresponding point is.

REVIEW

Understanding Graphing Coordinate Pairs

You can identify points on a coordinate plane using ordered pairs.

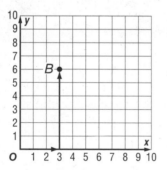

To identify the coordinates of point B, start at the origin. Move to the right along the x-axis until you are under the point. Count the number of units you moved. This is your x-coordinate. Now move up until you are at the point B. Count the number of units you moved. This is your y-coordinate. You can identify point B by the ordered pair (3, 6).

What You Should Know

Plotting points on a coordinate plane is similar to identifying points on a coordinate plane.

The coordinates of point D are (5, 2). To plot point D on a coordinate plane, start at the origin. Move to the right 5 units along the x-axis. Then move up 2 units. Draw a dot at that point and label it D.

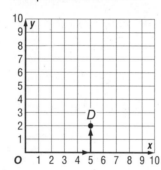

Identifying Points on a Coordinate Plane

Points on a coordinate plane can be identified using ordered pairs:

(x-coordinate, y-coordinate)

EXAMPLE 1

Name the ordered pair for point A.

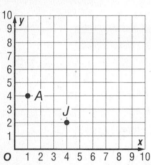

You can identify a point using its x-coordinate and its y-coordinate.

Start at the origin. Move to the right until you are under point A. Count the number of units you moved. This is your x-coordinate. Now move up until you are at point A. Count the number of units you moved. This is your y-coordinate. You can identify point A by the ordered pair (1, 4).

▶ **Understanding the Solution** Check your answer. Start at the origin. Move to the right 1 unit. Now move up 4 units. You should be at point A.

TRY IT!

Use the coordinate plane above to name the ordered pair of point J.

Plotting Points on a Coordinate Plane

You can use ordered pairs to plot points on a coordinate grid. The first number in the ordered pair, the x-coordinate, tells you how far to move to the right along the x-axis. The second number in the ordered pair, the y-coordinate, tells you how far to move up.

EXAMPLE 2

Plot and label the point M(6, 3) on a coordinate plane.

You can plot this point by moving to the right 6 units and up 3 units.

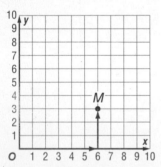

Start at the origin. Move to the right 6 units. Now move up 3 units. Draw a dot and label the point M.

Understanding the Solution Check your answer. Start at the origin. Move to the right 6 units. Now move up 3 units. You should be at point *M*.

TRY IT!

Plot and label the point *R*(2, 2) on a coordinate plane.

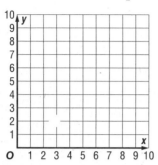

EXAMPLE 3

Suppose you start at the origin, move to the right 3 units and up 4 units. Make a dot. What is the ordered pair of the dot you made?

You can solve this problem by moving along the x-axis and then up to find the placement of the unknown point.

Start at the origin on a coordinate plane and move 3 units to the right. Then move 4 units up. Draw a dot.

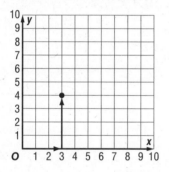

The ordered pair is (3, 4).

Understanding the Solution Since you started at the origin and moved three units along the *x*-axis, the *x*-coordinate is 3. Then you moved 4 units up, and the *y*-coordinate is 4.

TRY IT!

Leslie started at the origin, moved to the right 6 units and up no units. She made a dot. What is the ordered pair of the dot she made?

Exercises

1 Write the directions for locating the point (7, 1) on a coordinate plane.

Show your work.

Answer _____

_____

MULTIPLE CHOICE

2 Which point on the coordinate plane corresponds to the ordered pair (4, 4)?

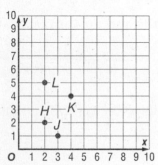

A Point *L*

B Point *K*

C Point *J*

D Point *H*

4 What are the coordinates of point *D*?

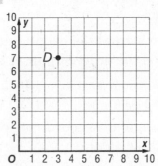

A (4, 6)

B (6, 4)

C (3, 7)

D (7, 3)

3 Which point on the coordinate plane corresponds to the ordered pair (0, 9)?

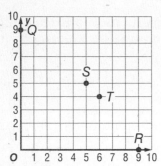

A Point *Q*

B Point *R*

C Point *S*

D Point *T*

5 What are the coordinates of point *V*?

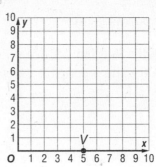

A (5, 0)

B (0, 5)

C (1, 5)

D (5, 1)

6 Suppose you start at the origin, then move 3 units to the right and 6 units up. Make a dot. Which ordered pair represents the dot you made?

   A (0, 9)

   B (9, 0)

   C (6, 3)

   D (3, 6)

7 Eli leaves his school located at (6, 4) and walks 2 units south of that point. What is the ordered pair of his new location?

   A (4, 4)

   B (6, 2)

   C (8, 4)

   D (6, 6)

EXTENDED RESPONSE

8 Use the coordinate plane below to record your work.

Part A

Start at the point (2, 2) on the coordinate plane. Move 1 unit to the right and 3 units up. Make a dot. What are the coordinates of your new point?

Show your work.

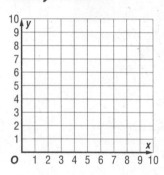

Answer _____

Part B

From your new point in Part A, move 2 units to the left and 3 units down. Make a dot. What is the ordered pair of your new point?

Show your work.

Answer _____

LESSON 2.2 Graphing Geometric Shapes

New York Performance Indicators

5.G.13 Plot points to form basic geometric shapes (identify and classify)

6.PS.7 Represent problem situations verbally, numerically, algebraically, and/or graphically

VOCABULARY

A **triangle** is a polygon with three sides and three angles.

A **rectangle** is a quadrilateral with four right angles; opposite sides are equal and parallel.

A **square** is a rectangle with four congruent sides.

A **parallelogram** is a quadrilateral in which each pair of opposite sides is parallel and equal in length.

REVIEW

Understanding Graphing Geometric Shapes

By plotting several points and connecting the points with line segments, you can make shapes.

Plot the points (2, 2), (6, 2), and (0, 4). Connect the three points to form a geographic figure. Identify the shape you graphed.

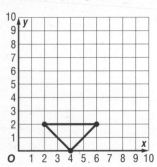

The shape graphed is a triangle.

Applying Graphing Geometric Shapes

Three corners of a rectangle graphed on a coordinate plane are (1, 1), (1, 3), and (5, 3). What is the ordered pair of the fourth corner?

Start by plotting the three known points on a coordinate plane. Then sketch the rectangle. This will allow you to locate the fourth point.

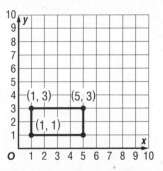

Now you can identify the coordinates of the fourth corner of the rectangle. Move to the right 5 units and up 1 unit. The ordered pair of the fourth corner is (5, 1).

Identify Geometric Shapes

You can graph and identify geometric shapes on a coordinate plane.

EXAMPLE 1

Identify the shape formed by connecting the following points in the order listed: (3, 4), (5, 7), (10, 7), and (8, 4).

You can solve this problem by plotting and connecting the points in the order listed. Start by plotting all four points on a coordinate plane. Connect the points in the order listed. Be sure to connect the last point to the first point.

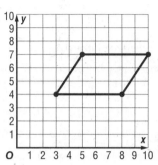

Now you can identify the shape. It is a parallelogram.

▶ **Understanding the Solution**   The shape you graphed has four sides in which each pair of opposite sides is parallel and equal in length. The shape is a parallelogram.

TRY IT!

Identify the shape formed by connecting the following points in the order listed: (3, 1), (3, 4), (6, 4), and (6, 1).

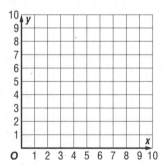

EXAMPLE 2

Roger is planning to make a new square pen for his dog in his backyard. He draws his plans for the dog pen on a coordinate plane and connects each pair of points. Three of the four corners of the pen are located at (0, 1), (3, 1), and (3, 4). What is the ordered pair of the fourth corner of the pen?

You can solve this problem by plotting the three known points on a coordinate plane and finding the placement of the unknown point.

Start by plotting the three known points on a coordinate plane and drawing the square. This will allow you to locate the fourth point.

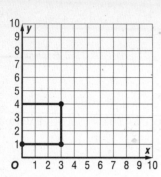

Now you can identify and name the fourth corner of the square. Move to the right 0 units and up 4 units. The ordered pair of the fourth corner is (0, 4).

▶ **Understanding the Solution**   The pen Roger is planning to build is square. All sides should be the same length. Look at your coordinate plane to make sure all sides of your square are the same length.

TRY IT!

Leslie plotted the points (1, 0), (3, 3), and (5, 0) and connected the points. What shape did she draw?

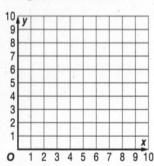

Exercises

SHORT RESPONSE

1 Plot the points (1, 1), (1, 5), (3, 5), and (3, 1). Connect the points in the order they are listed. What shape have you drawn?

Show your work.

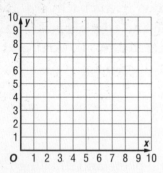

Answer _____

2 What letter is formed if you plot the points (2, 5), (2, 1), (5, 1), (5, 2), (3, 2), and (3, 5) and connect the points in the order listed?

A H

B I

C K

D L

5 What shape is formed if you plot the points (1, 1), (3, 1), and (2, 6) and connect the points in the order listed?

A rectangle

B square

C triangle

D parallelogram

3 What shape is formed if you plot the points (0, 0), (2, 0), (2, 2), and (0, 2) and connect the points in the order listed?

A rectangle

B square

C triangle

D parallelogram

6 Three corners of a rectangle plotted on a coordinate plane are (4, 1), (6, 1), and (6, 6). What is the ordered pair of the fourth corner?

A (4, 6)

B (6, 4)

C (3, 6)

D (6, 3)

4 Matthew plots three points and connects them as shown on the coordinate plane below.

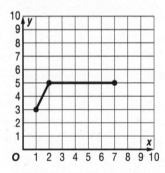

What are the coordinates of the point Matthew should plot next if he wants to draw a parallelogram?

A (7, 3)

B (3, 7)

C (6, 3)

D (3, 6)

7 Josephina plots three points and connects them as shown on the coordinate plane below.

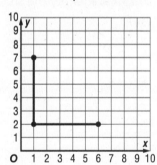

What coordinates should Josephina plot next if she wants to draw a square?

A (7, 6)

B (6, 7)

C (6, 6)

D (7, 7)

8 Use the coordinate plane below to record your work.

Part A

Locate 4 points on the coordinate plane that form a square, a rectangle, or a parallelogram. Plot the points on the coordinate plane. Label each point with a letter. On a separate sheet of paper, write the ordered pair for each point you plotted.

Show your work.

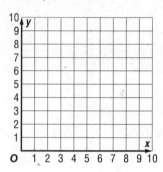

Answer_____

Part B

Exchange your list of ordered pairs with another student in the class. Ask him or her to graph the points and identify the shape graphed.

Show your work.

Answer _____

LESSON 2.3 Finding Perimeter

New York Performance Indicators

5.G.14 Calculate perimeter of basic geometric shapes drawn on a coordinate plane (rectangles and shapes composed of rectangles having sides with integer lengths and parallel to the axes)

6.PS.7 Represent problem situations verbally, numerically, algebraically, and/or graphically

VOCABULARY

The **perimeter** is the distance around a shape or region.

REVIEW

Understanding Perimeter

The distance around a shape or closed figure is its perimeter. The perimeter of a figure can be found by adding the lengths of each of its sides.

The perimeter P of a square is 4 times the length of one side s.

$$P = 4s$$

The perimeter of a square that measures 4 centimeters on each side is

$$P = 4s$$
$$P = 4(4)$$
$$P = 16 \text{ centimeters}$$

The perimeter P of a rectangle is 2 times the length ℓ plus 2 times the width w.

$$P = 2\ell + 2w$$

The perimeter of the rectangle below is

3 in.

5 in.

$$P = 2\ell + 2w$$
$$P = 2(5) + 2(3)$$
$$P = 10 + 6$$
$$P = 16 \text{ inches}$$

Applying Understanding Perimeter

The figure below is an outline of Jake's bedroom. Find the perimeter of the room. Each unit represents 1 foot.

Jake's Room

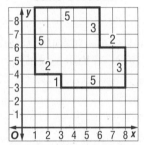

Start by counting and labeling the length of each side of the room. Since the figure is not a rectangle or a square, you cannot use a formula to find the perimeter. You can find the perimeter of Jake's room by adding the lengths of all the sides.

$$P = 5 + 3 + 2 + 3 + 5 + 1 + 2 + 5$$
$$= 26 \text{ feet}$$

The perimeter of Jake's room is 26 feet.

Finding the Perimeter of a Geometric Shape

The perimeter of a shape or figure can be found using a formula or by adding the lengths of all the sides. If the figure is a square, use the formula $P = 4s$. If the figure is a rectangle, use the formula $P = 2\ell + 2w$. If the figure has an irregular shape or is neither a square nor rectangle, add the lengths of the sides to find the perimeter.

EXAMPLE 1

Find the perimeter of the rectangle.

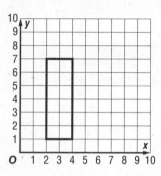

You can solve this problem by using the formula for perimeter of a rectangle.
The formula for perimeter of a rectangle is $P = 2\ell + 2w$. The length of the rectangle is 6 units, and the width is 2 units. Substitute those values into the formula for ℓ and w and solve.

$$P = 2\ell + 2w$$
$$P = 2(6) + 2(2)$$
$$P = 12 + 4$$
$$P = 16 \text{ units}$$

▶ **Understanding the Solution**   The distance around the rectangle is 16 units. You can check your answer by adding the lengths of all the sides. $P = 2 + 6 + 2 + 6 = 16$ units

TRY IT!

Find the perimeter of the square.

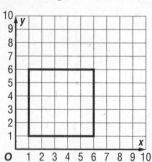

EXAMPLE 2

Diego drew a diagram of his closet on a coordinate plane.

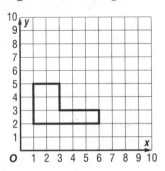

Find the perimeter of the closet. One unit equals 1 foot.

You can solve this problem by adding the lengths of all the sides.

Find the lengths of all the sides of Diego's closet. Find the sum of the lengths.
$P = 3 + 5 + 1 + 3 + 2 + 2 = 16$ feet

▶ **Understanding the Solution** The perimeter of Diego's closet is 16 feet.

TRY IT!

Find the perimeter of the figure below. One unit equals 1 meter.

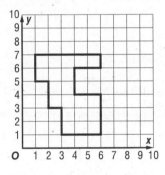

Exercises

SHORT RESPONSE

1 Describe how you would find the perimeter of a rectangle with a length of 9 units and a width of 7 units. Find the perimeter.

Show your work.

Answer _____

_____

2 Find the perimeter of the figure below.

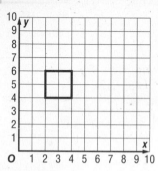

A 2 units

B 4 units

C 6 units

D 8 units

3 Find the perimeter of the figure below.

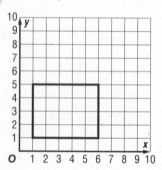

A 4 units

B 5 units

C 18 units

D 20 units

4 Find the perimeter of the figure below.

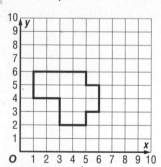

A 17 units

B 18 units

C 19 units

D 20 units

5 Find the perimeter of the figure below.

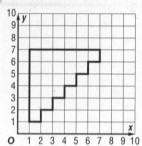

A 18 units

B 20 units

C 22 units

D 24 units

6 Beth drew a diagram of her bedroom on a coordinate plane.

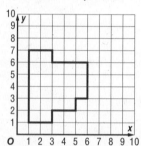

What is the perimeter of the bedroom?
1 unit = 1 foot

A 20 feet

B 21 feet

C 22 feet

D 23 feet

7 Mrs. Brothers drew a diagram of her classroom on a coordinate plane.

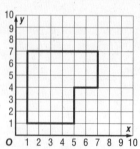

What is the perimeter of the classroom?
1 unit = 1 yard

A 18 yards

B 20 yards

C 22 yards

D 24 yards

8 Use the coordinate plane below to show your work.

Part A

Graph and connect the following points in the order listed to create a closed figure: (1, 1), (1, 4), (2, 4), (2, 6), (4, 6), (4, 1), (1, 1).

Show your work.

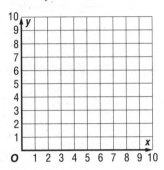

Answer _____

Part B

Find the perimeter of the figure you graphed in Part A.

Show your work.

Answer _____

LESSON 2.4 · *Problem-Solving Strategy: Drawing a Picture*

New York Performance Indicators

6.PS.2 Understand some ways of representing a problem are more efficient than others

6.PS.13 Model problems with pictures/diagrams or physical objects

Understand the Strategy

Drawing pictures or diagrams can help you solve some problems. Being able to see what is happening in a situation is often very helpful.

Problem

Maxine is helping to decorate a rectangular room for the Fall Festival at school. Maxine was asked to hang streamers from each corner of the room to every other corner of the room. How many streamers will she need?

Solution

What do you know?

There are four corners in the room.
The room is rectangular in shape.
A streamer needs to go from each corner to every other corner.

What do you need to find?

How many streamers will she need?

Find the relationship.

Begin this problem by drawing a diagram of the four corners of the room.

• •   •

•   •

Now draw lines to represent the streamers that Maxine will hang from the corners.

To find the number of streamers Maxine will need, count the number of lines you drew on your diagram. There are 6 lines.

▶ **Understanding the Solution**   You drew 6 lines to represent the streamers that Maxine needed to hang in the classroom. So Maxine will need 6 streamers to decorate the room.

Exercises

1 A new hamburger shop just opened. They are offering 2 different kinds of buns and 5 different toppings. How many different hamburgers can you make using 1 type of bun and 1 topping? Draw a picture or diagram to solve.

Show your work.

Answer _____

2 Jasmin is planting a garden in her backyard. The garden is 14 feet long. She wants to plant one row of beans the entire length of the garden. She wants to plant a seed at each end of the row and every 2 feet along the row. How many seeds will she need? Draw a picture or diagram to solve.

Show your work.

Answer _____

MULTIPLE CHOICE

1 Which point on the coordinate plane corresponds to the ordered pair (0, 5)?

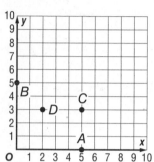

A Point *A*
B Point *B*
C Point *C*
D Point *D*

2 What are the coordinates of point *V*?

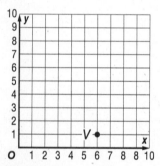

A (6, 1)
B (1, 6)
C (1, 5)
D (5, 1)

3 What shape is formed if you plot the points (2, 5), (6, 5), (5, 3), and (1, 3) and connect the points in the order listed?

A rectangle
B square
C triangle
D parallelogram

4 Hamal plots three points and connects them as shown on the coordinate plane below.

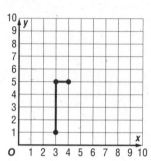

What ordered pair should Hamal plot next if he wants to draw a rectangle?

A (5, 2)   B (1, 4)
C (4, 1)   D (3, 2)

5 Find the perimeter of the figure below.

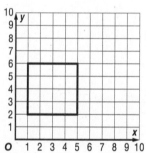

A 4 units   B 12 units
C 16 units   D 20 units

6 On the grid below is a diagram of a living room.

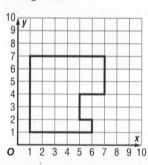

What is the perimeter of the room?
1 unit = 2 feet

A 25 feet   B 26 feet
C 50 feet   D 52 feet

7 Use the coordinate plane below to record your work.

PART A

Plot the point (4, 3) on the coordinate plane. Now move 2 units to the left and 4 units up. Make a dot. What are the coordinates of your new point?

Show your work.

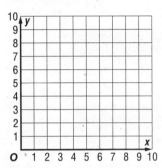

Answer _____

PART B

From your new point in Part A, move 5 units to the right and 2 units down. Make a dot. What are the coordinates of your new point?

Show your work.

Answer _____

PART C

You should now have three points on your graph. Connect each pair of points. What shape is formed?

Show your work.

Answer _____

LESSON 3.1 Outcomes of Simple Events

 New York Performance Indicators

5.S.5 List the possible outcomes for a single-event experiment
5.S.6 Record experiment results using fractions/ratios
6.PS.17 Determine what information is needed to solve a problem

VOCABULARY

An **outcome** is a possible result of an experiment.

An **event** is a set of outcomes in a probability experiment.

REVIEW

Understanding Outcomes of Simple Events

An outcome of an event is a possible result.

Suppose you roll a number cube once. What are the possible outcomes when you roll the number cube?

You could roll a 1, 2, 3, 4, 5, or 6. So there are 6 possible outcomes when you roll a number cube.

Applying Outcomes of Simple Events

There are 5 marbles in a bag. Only one is green. What fraction of the marbles in the bag is green?

$$\frac{\text{Number of green marbles in the bag}}{\text{Number of marbles in the bag}} = \frac{1}{5}$$

Listing Possible Outcomes

The possible outcomes of an event are all the possible results of the event. For example, when you flip a coin, there are 2 possible outcomes. You can get a head or you can get a tail.

EXAMPLE 1

In a drawer there is 1 pair of green socks, 2 pairs of blue socks, 1 pair of red socks, and 1 pair of white socks. You randomly choose 1 pair of socks out of the drawer. List all the possible outcomes.

You can solve this problem by making a list.

Think about what could happen if you were actually choosing a pair of socks out of the drawer. You could choose a green pair, a blue pair, a red pair, or a white pair.

▶ **Understanding the Solution** There are 4 possible outcomes if you randomly choose 1 pair of socks from the drawer.

TRY IT!

There is a bag containing 5 tiles, each marked with a different vowel. What are the possible outcomes if you randomly choose 1 tile from the bag?

Recording Results of an Experiment

You can record results of an experiment using fractions and ratios.

EXAMPLE 2

Jamie rolled a number cube 8 times. Her results are recorded in the table below. What fraction of the rolls was an even number?

Number on Number Cube	Number of Times Rolled
1	2
2	0
3	0
4	1
5	3
6	2

You can solve this problem using the information given in the table.
How many times was an even number rolled? 3 times.

How many times was the number cube rolled? 8 times.

▶ **Understanding the Solution**   In the experiment of rolling the number cube, $\frac{3}{8}$ of the rolls resulted in landing on an even number.

TRY IT!

Use the table in the example. What is the ratio of even rolls to odd rolls?

Exercises

SHORT RESPONSE

1 A bag contains 12 pieces of paper, each labeled with a different month of the year. What are the possible outcomes of drawing a month beginning with the letter A?

Show your work.

Answer _____

2 You spin a spinner that is divided into 8 equal sections. Each section is labeled with a different number 1 through 8. How many possible outcomes are there?

A 2

B 4

C 6

D 8

3 You flip two coins. How many possible outcomes are there?

A 1

B 2

C 4

D 8

4 You roll a number cube. How many possible outcomes are even numbers?

A 2

B 3

C 4

D 8

5 A spinner is divided into six equal sections. Two sections are green, two sections are blue, and two sections are yellow. What is the ratio of yellow sections to total sections?

A 2 : 6

B 1 : 6

C 3 : 6

D 4 : 6

6 There is a bag containing 26 tiles, each marked with a different letter of the alphabet. What is the ratio of vowel tiles to consonant tiles?

A 1 : 21

B 5 : 21

C 21 : 26

D 25 : 26

7 You randomly choose 1 T-shirt out of a drawer. In the drawer there is 1 long sleeve T-shirt, 2 short sleeve T-shirts, and 5 sleeveless T-shirts. What fraction of the shirts is sleeveless?

A $\frac{5}{8}$

B $\frac{8}{5}$

C $\frac{2}{8}$

D $\frac{5}{3}$

8 There are 6 marbles in a bag. One is green, two are red, and three are blue. What fraction of the marbles is red?

A $\frac{1}{6}$

B $\frac{1}{3}$

C $\frac{1}{2}$

D $\frac{2}{3}$

REREAD EXERCISE 8.

9 If you remove one red marble from the bag and add one blue marble, what fraction of the marbles is blue?

A $\frac{1}{6}$

B $\frac{1}{3}$

C $\frac{1}{2}$

D $\frac{2}{3}$

10 Janice drew one card from a standard deck of 52 cards.

Part A

How many possible outcomes are there?

Show your work.

Answer _____

Part B

What fraction of the deck of cards is red?

Show your work.

Answer _____

Part C

What is the ratio of aces to the total number of cards in the deck?

Show your work.

Answer _____

LESSON 3.2 Sample Space and Probability

New York Performance Indicators

5.S.7 Create a sample space and determine probability of a single event, given a simple experiment (i.e., rolling a number cube)

6.PS.9 Understand the basic language of logic in mathematical situations (and, or, not)

6.PS.15 Make organized lists or charts to solve numerical problems

VOCABULARY

Probability is the chance that some event will occur.

A **sample space** is the set of all possible outcomes in a probability experiment.

REVIEW

Understanding Sample Space and Probability

A list of all of the possible outcomes of an event is called the sample space for that event. The sample space for flipping a coin is heads and tails. They are the 2 possible outcomes of flipping a coin.

The probability of an event is the likeliness of the event happening. It is the ratio that compares the number of favorable outcomes to the number of possible outcomes.

$$P(\text{event}) = \frac{\text{number of favorable outcomes}}{\text{number of possible outcomes}}$$

What You Should Know

- The probability of an event occurring is a number from 0 to 1, including 0 and 1.
- A probability of 0 means the outcome is impossible. A probability of 1 means the outcome is certain to happen.

Example

- When rolling a standard number cube, the probability of rolling a 7 is 0 since no side has a 7 on it.
- When flipping a coin, it is certain that you will either toss a head or a tail. Therefore, the probability of tossing a head *or* a tail is 1.

Sample Space

The sample space of an event is all the possible outcomes. In other words, the sample space shows all the things that could happen during the event.

EXAMPLE 1

Five cards are placed face down on a table. There is a 2, a 5, an ace, a jack, and a king. You are asked to draw one card from the pile. What is the sample space for this event?

You can solve this problem by making an organized list of all the possible outcomes of drawing one card.

Make a list of the cards you could draw.

    2, 5, ace, jack, king

▶ **Understanding the Solution** There are 5 possible outcomes.

TRY IT!

A bag contains 10 colored gems: 1 yellow, 1 green, 2 silver, 1 black, 3 red, 1 white, and 1 blue. Fernando drew one gem from the bag. What is the sample space for this event?

Probability

The probability of an event is the chance that the event will occur.

$$P(\text{event}) = \frac{\text{number of favorable outcomes}}{\text{number of possible outcomes}}$$

EXAMPLE 2

You roll a number cube. What is the probability of rolling a 2?

You can solve this problem using the formula below.

$$P(\text{event}) = \frac{\text{number of favorable outcomes}}{\text{number of possible outcomes}}$$

How many favorable outcomes are there? In other words, how many ways can you roll a 2 using one number cube? There is 1 way.

How many possible outcomes are there? You could roll a 1, 2, 3, 4, 5, or 6. There are 6 possible outcomes.

$$P(\text{event}) = \frac{\text{number of favorable outcomes}}{\text{number of possible outcomes}}$$
$$= \frac{1}{6}$$

So the probability of rolling a 2 is $\frac{1}{6}$.

▶ **Understanding the Solution**   The probability of rolling a 2 is $\frac{1}{6}$. This ratio $\frac{1}{6}$ compares the number of favorable outcomes to the total number of outcomes.

TRY IT!

You roll a number cube. What is the probability of rolling a 3 or 6?

Exercises

1 You roll a number cube one time. What is the probability of rolling a 3 and a 4? Explain your answer.

Show your work.

Answer _____

_____

MULTIPLE CHOICE

2 There are 5 bingo chips in a bag. 1 is white, 2 are blue, and 2 are red. If you randomly pull one bingo chip out of the bag, what is the probability that it will be a blue bingo chip?

A $\frac{1}{5}$

B $\frac{2}{5}$

C $\frac{3}{5}$

D $\frac{4}{5}$

3 There is a bag containing 26 small pieces of paper, each marked with a different letter of the alphabet. You are asked to randomly pull one piece of paper out of the bag. How many outcomes are in the sample space of this event?

A 1
B 5
C 25
D 26

4 You randomly choose a scarf out of a drawer. In the drawer there is 1 plaid scarf, 2 scarves with stripes, and 5 scarves with patterns on them. What is the probability of choosing a scarf that is not plaid?

A $\frac{5}{8}$

B $\frac{7}{8}$

C $\frac{8}{7}$

D $\frac{8}{5}$

5 You roll a number cube. What is the probability of rolling an even number?

A $\frac{1}{6}$

B $\frac{1}{3}$

C $\frac{1}{2}$

D $\frac{2}{3}$

6 The probability that September will have 31 days this year is

A 1

B $\frac{1}{2}$

C $\frac{1}{31}$

D 0

7 What is the probability of rolling an odd number or an even number on a number cube?

A 0

B $\frac{1}{6}$

C $\frac{5}{6}$

D 1

8 The science club at school is holding a raffle as a fund-raiser. The tickets are $10 each, and the winner will receive a prize. Only 100 tickets will be sold.

Part A
If you buy 1 ticket, what is the probability that you will win the prize?
Show your work.

Answer _____

Part B
If you buy 5 tickets, what is the probability that you will win the prize?
Show your work.

Answer _____

Problem-Solving Strategy: Drawing a Diagram

New York Performance Indicators

6.PS.15 Make organized lists or charts to solve numerical problems

6.R.1 Use physical objects, drawings, charts, tables, graphs, symbols, equations, or objects created using technology as representations

6.R.2 Explain, describe, and defend mathematical ideas using representations

Understand the Strategy

When solving word problems, sometimes it can be helpful to draw a diagram. Diagrams are good ways to organize information.

Problem: Ben, Quinn, and Alex are all friends. In how many different ways can these friends be arranged in a row?

SOLUTION

What do you know?

There are three friends.

They are to be arranged in a row.

What do you need to find?

How many different ways can they be arranged in a row?

Find the relationship.

To solve this problem, it may be helpful to draw a tree diagram.

1st in line	2nd in line	3rd in line
Ben	Quinn	Alex
	Alex	Quinn
Quinn	Ben	Alex
	Alex	Ben
Alex	Quinn	Ben
	Ben	Quinn

▶ **Understanding the Solution**   You can use the diagram to count the number of different possibilities there are. There are 6 different ways the friends can be arranged in a row.

1 How many salad and dressing combinations are possible if you have the choice of cobb salad, chef salad, or Asian salad with ranch, blue cheese, or Italian dressing? Draw a tree diagram to help you find the answer.

Show your work.

Answer _____

2 Marietta opened a new sandwich shop. She offers 3 choices of meat, 2 different toppings and 2 different sauces. She claims that there are over 15 different sandwich combinations she can make. Is her claim true? Defend your answer using a diagram.

Show your work.

Answer _____

MULTIPLE CHOICE

1 You spin a spinner that is divided into 8 equal sections. Each section is labeled with a different letter A through H. How many possible outcomes are there?

A 2
B 4
C 6
D 8

2 There are 9 marbles in a bag. One is green, two are red, five are white, and one is blue. What fraction of the marbles is white?

A $\frac{2}{9}$
B $\frac{3}{9}$
C $\frac{4}{9}$
D $\frac{5}{9}$

3 There are 5 blocks in a bag. Only two are black. If you randomly pull one block out of the bag, what is the probability that it will not be a black block?

A $\frac{1}{5}$
B $\frac{2}{5}$
C $\frac{3}{5}$
D $\frac{4}{5}$

4 Several cards are placed face down on a table in a pile. There is a 2, a 5, a 6, an 8, an ace, a jack, and a king. You are asked to draw one card from the pile. How many outcomes are in the sample space for this event?

A 2
B 3
C 6
D 7

5 A bag contains 26 small pieces of paper, each marked with a different letter of the alphabet. If you randomly pull one piece of paper out of the bag, what is the probability that it will be an M, an X, or a T?

A $\frac{1}{26}$
B $\frac{3}{26}$
C $\frac{23}{26}$
D $\frac{26}{3}$

6 A box contains 9 tiles, each marked with a different number 1–9. What is the ratio of even numbers to odd numbers?

A 4 : 9
B 5 : 9
C 4 : 5
D 5 : 4

7 Issa sells handmade hats. She has green, red, and pink hats in sizes small, medium, and large. How many possible combinations of hat color and size are there?

Part A

Draw a tree diagram to show all the possible combinations of hat color and size.
Show your work.

Answer _____

Part B

How many possible combinations of hat color and size are there?
Show your work.

Answer _____

8 Use what you know about probability to answer part A and part B.

Part A

What does it mean when an event has a probability of 1? Give an example of an event that has a probability of 1.
Show your work.

Answer _____

_____

Part B

What does it mean when an event has a probability of 0? Give an example of an event that has a probability of 0.
Show your work.

Answer _____

_____

PART 1

1 Which algebraic expression represents the verbal expression "the sum of 12 and a number?"

A $n - 12$

B $12 - n$

C $12 + n$

D $12 \div n$

2 Evaluate the expression $13 - k$ for $k = 3$.

A 6

B 10

C 16

D 39

3 Which is a solution to the equation $r + 15 = 40$?

A 25

B 45

C 55

D 600

4 Ramira has 4 more stickers than her friend Sam. Sam has 2 stickers. How many stickers r does Ramira have if the equation $r - 4 = 2$ represents this situation?

A 1

B 2

C 6

D 8

5 Famika flipped a coin six times. Her results are recorded in the table below. What fraction of the flips were tails?

Flip	Heads or Tails
1	heads
2	heads
3	tails
4	heads
5	tails
6	heads

A $\frac{2}{3}$

B $\frac{1}{2}$

C $\frac{1}{3}$

D $\frac{1}{5}$

6 What are the coordinates of point M?

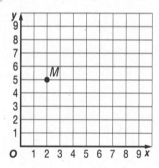

A (2, 5)

B (6, 4)

C (3, 7)

D (7, 3)

7 Lily leaves the library located at (6, 5) and walks 3 units north of that point. What is the ordered pair of her new location?

A (6, 2)

B (9, 5)

C (3, 5)

D (6, 8)

8 What shape is formed if you plot the points (0, 2), (4, 2), (4, 0), and (0, 0) and connect the points in the order listed?

    A rectangle

    B square

    C triangle

    D parallelogram

9 Three corners of a parallelogram graphed on a coordinate plane are (2, 2), (2, 5), and (4, 4). Which can be an ordered pair of the fourth corner?

    A (4, 1)

    B (4, 2)

    C (1, 4)

    D (2, 4)

10 Find the perimeter of the figure below.

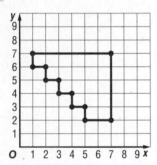

    A 18 units

    B 20 units

    C 22 units

    D 24 units

11 On the grid below, Barry drew a diagram of his basement.

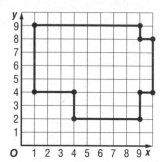

What is the perimeter of the basement? 1 unit = 1 yard

A 28 yards

B 30 yards

C 32 yards

D 34 yards

12 You flip a coin. How many possible outcomes are there?

A 1

B 2

C 3

D 4

13 There are 7 beans in a bag. One is brown, three are white, and three are black. What fraction of the beans is brown?

A $\frac{1}{7}$

B $\frac{1}{6}$

C $\frac{3}{7}$

D 3

14 There are 10 beads in a bag. One is white, two are blue, four are silver, and three are red. If you randomly pull one bead out of the bag, what is the probability that it will be blue?

A $\frac{1}{10}$

B $\frac{1}{5}$

C $\frac{3}{10}$

D $\frac{2}{5}$

15 Use the coordinate plane below to name the ordered pair for point *K*.

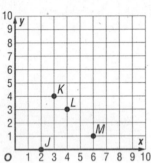

A (6, 1)

B (4, 3)

C (3, 4)

D (2, 0)

16 A bag contains 8 wooden disks, each marked with a different letter in the word *GEOMETRY*. You are asked to randomly pull one disk out of the bag. How many outcomes are in the sample space of this event?

A 6

B 7

C 8

D 9

17 Park officials would like to put a fence around a square play area in the city park.

Part A

Write an algebraic expression for the perimeter of the play area. Let $s =$ the length of one side of the play area.

Show your work.

Answer _____

Part B

If the length of one side of the play area is 35 feet long, what is the perimeter of the area?

Show your work.

Answer _____

18 Use the equation $n - 95 = 325$ to answer the following questions.

Part A

Describe how you could use inverse operations to solve the equation.

Show your work.

Answer _____

Part B

Solve the equation.

Show your work.

Answer _____

19 Use the coordinate plane below to record your work.

Part A

Start at the point (0, 5) on the coordinate plane. Move 4 units to the right and 2 units down. Make a dot. What is the ordered pair of your new point?

Show your work.

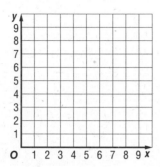

Answer _____

Part B

From your new point in Part A, move 2 units to the left and 4 units up. Make a dot. What is the ordered pair of your new point?

Show your work.

Answer _____

20 Use the coordinate plane below to record your work.

Part A

Plot the points (1, 1), (1, 4), and (4, 4) on the coordinate plane. Connect the points in the order they are listed.

Show your work.

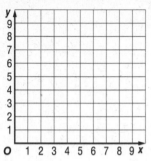

Answer _____

Part B

What is the ordered pair of the fourth point that would make that figure a square?

Show your work.

Answer _____

21 Use the coordinate plane below to show your work.

Part A

Graph the points (1, 1), (4, 1), (4, 2), (6, 2), (6, 5), and (1, 5) on the coordinate plane below. Connect the points in the order listed to make a closed figure.

Show your work.

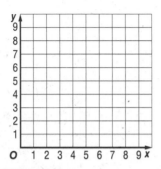

Answer _____

Part B

Find the perimeter of the figure you graphed in Part A.

Show your work.

Answer _____

22 Janice rolled one number cube.

Part A

How many possible outcomes are there? What are the outcomes?

Show your work.

Answer _____

Part B

What fraction of the outcomes are prime numbers?

Show your work.

Answer _____

23 The PTA always draws for attendance prizes at the meetings. There were 129 people at the meeting, and each person got 1 ticket. One ticket will be drawn at random for the attendance prize.

Part A

If you have 1 ticket, what is the probability that you will win the prize?

Show your work.

Answer _____

Part B

If you, and two of your friends attended the meeting and each got a ticket, what is the probability that someone in your group will win the prize?

Show your work.

Answer _____

Whole Numbers to Trillions

LESSON 4.1   Whole Numbers to Trillions

New York Performance Indicators

6.N.1   Read and write whole numbers to trillions

6.PS.7   Represent problem situations verbally, numerically, algebraically, and/or graphically

6.PS.8   Select an appropriate representation of a problem

VOCABULARY

Standard form/standard notation is the usual way of writing a number that shows only its digits, no words.

A **period** is a three-digit group of numbers from a place-value chart.

A **digit** is a symbol used to write a number. The ten digits are 0, 1, 2, 3, 4, 5, 6, 7, 8, 9.

Expanded form/expanded notation represents a number as a sum that shows the value of each digit.

REVIEW

Understanding Numbers to Trillions

- Numbers to trillions involve four periods.
- The periods from greatest to least are billions, millions, thousands, and ones.
- The places within periods repeat: hundreds, tens, ones, hundreds, tens, ones, etc.

Billions Period			Millions Period			Thousands Period			Ones Period		
hundreds	tens	ones	hundreds	tens	ones	hundreds	tens	ones	hundreds	tens	ones

What You Should Know

- Commas are used to separate the periods within a number.
- To read and write numbers, it is helpful to know the period and the place within the period.
- Each digit in a number has a place value that depends on the location or place within the number.

Example

Consider the following number:

30,060,127,800

- This number is written in standard form.
- The word form of the number is thirty billion, sixty million, one hundred twenty-seven thousand, eight hundred.
- The expanded form of the number is: 30,000,000,000 + 60,000,000 + 100,000 + 20,000 + 7,000 + 800.

Reading and Writing Whole Numbers

Numbers can be expressed in several forms. Three of the forms are standard, word, and expanded. If a number is given in one form, then the other two forms can be determined.

58   Chapter 4 Number Sense and Operations

EXAMPLE 1

The world population was estimated at 6,446,131,400 people in July 2005. Express the world population number in two other forms.

You can solve this problem by expressing the number in word and expanded form.
To write the number in word form, begin with the digits at the far left side of the number and write the numbers in each period in word form followed by the name of the period. Use a comma to separate the periods just as in the number.

six billion, four hundred forty-six million,
one hundred thirty-one thousand, four hundred

To write the number in expanded form, write the value of each digit and connect the values with plus signs to form a sum.

$$6,000,000,000 + 400,000,000 + 40,000,000 +$$
$$6,000,000 + 100,000 + 30,000 + 1,000 + 400$$

▶ Understanding the Solution The number 6,446,131,400 has four periods, therefore the number is in the billions. Writing the number is just like reading it. Begin with the 6 in the billions place. Follow it with each of the next three periods, along with their place value, until the end of the number is reached.

Expanded form requires an addend for each nonzero digit in the number. Its value is based upon its place in the number. Since there are eight nonzero digits in the number, there are eight addends in the expanded form.

TRY IT!

Brooke found the sum of a group of numbers to be 350,700,104,008. How would she express this number in two other forms?

EXAMPLE 2

The volume of the Earth's moon is twenty-one billion, nine hundred seventy million cubic kilometers. Express this number in two other forms.

You can solve this problem by expressing the number in standard and expanded form.
To write the number in standard form, write the digits that the words represent. Place commas in the same place as they appear in the word form. Fill in with zeros to show all of the necessary periods if words are not present for their places.

21,970,000,000

Use the standard form to write the number in expanded form. Remember to write the answer as the sum of the place values of each nonzero digit.

$$20,000,000,000 + 1,000,000,000 + 900,000,000 + 70,000,000$$

▶ **Understanding the Solution** The words in the number only give digits for the billions and millions period. There aren't any words in the number to account for the periods after the millions, so it becomes necessary to fill in three zeros for the thousands period and three zeros for the ones period. The other digits are represented by words. The expanded form will only have four addends because there are only four nonzero digits in the number.

TRY IT!

The planet Mars has an orbital circumference of one billion, three hundred sixty-six million, nine hundred thousand kilometers. Express this number in two other forms.

EXAMPLE 3

A sixth grade teacher wrote a number in expanded form on the board. She asked the class to write the number in two other forms. Write the number in the two forms.

$$500,000,000,000 + 1,000,000,000 + 400,000 + 30$$

You can solve this problem by writing the numbers in standard and word form.
To write the number in standard form, add the numbers.

$$
\begin{array}{r}
500,000,000,000 \\
1,000,000,000 \\
400,000 \\
+ \qquad 30 \\
\hline
501,000,400,030
\end{array}
$$

Take the standard form of the number and write it in words.

Five hundred one billion, four hundred thousand, thirty

▶ **Understanding the Solution** The value of each digit in your answer should be the same as the values given in the problem. Also, the expanded form of the number has four addends, so the standard form should have four nonzero digits. The standard form of the number has four periods because of the four groups of three numbers that are separated by commas. There aren't any millions because of the three zeros in the millions period. Thus when written in words, only the billions, thousands, and ones periods are given.

TRY IT!

Write the following number in standard and word form.

$$700,000,000,000 + 50,000,000 + 3,000,000 + 20,000 + 8,000$$

Exercises

SHORT RESPONSE

1 Neptune is four billion, four hundred ninety-eight million, two hundred fifty-two thousand, nine hundred kilometers from the Sun. Express this number in expanded form.

Show your work.

Answer _____

_____

MULTIPLE CHOICE

2 Which correctly gives thirty-six billion, eighteen million, one hundred seven in expanded form?

 A 30,000,000,000 + 6,000,000,000 + 100,000,000 + 8,000,000 + 1,000 + 7

 B 30,000,000 + 6,000,000 + 10,000 + 8,000 + 107

 C 30,000,000 + 6,000,000 + 100,000 + 80,000 + 100 + 7

 D 30,000,000,000 + 6,000,000,000 + 10,000,000 + 8,000,000 + 100 + 7

3 The top three movies of all time earned a total of one billion, four hundred ninety-two million, nine hundred thousand dollars. Which represents this number in standard form?

 A $1,492,900,000

 B $10,492,900,000

 C $1,492,900

 D $1,492,000,900

4 Saturn has a surface area of 40,000,000,000 + 3,000,000,000 + 400,000,000 + 60,000,000 + 6,000,000 square kilometers. Which correctly gives this number in word form?

 A forty-three million, four hundred sixty-six

 B forty-three billion, four hundred sixty-six thousand

 C forty-three billion, four hundred sixty-six million

 D forty-three, four hundred sixty-six

5 Which of the following is the word form of 304,000,005,049?

 A three hundred four, five thousand, forty-nine

 B three hundred four billion, five thousand, forty-nine

 C three hundred four million, five hundred, forty-nine

 D three billion, four million, five thousand, forty-nine

6 What is 6,000,000,000 + 80,000,000 + 60,000 + 3,000 + 200 + 9 in standard form?

 A 6,080,063,209

 B 6,863,000,209

 C 6,080,630,209

 D 6,080,603,209

7 What is 905,008,004,701 written in expanded form?

 A 900,000,000,000 + 8,000,000 + 4,000 + 700 + 1

 B 900,000,000,000 + 5,000,000,000 + 8,000,000 + 4,000 + 700 + 1

 C 90,000,000,000 + 5,000,000,000 + 8,000,000 + 4,000 + 701

 D 905,000,000,000 + 8,000,000,000 + 40,000 + 700

8 A person who lives to be 83 years old will have lived about 2,617,488,000 seconds.

Part A

Write the number of seconds in word form.

Show your work.

Answer _____

Part B

Write the number of seconds in expanded form.

Show your work.

Answer _____

_____

LESSON 4.2 Addition and Multiplication Properties

New York Performance Indicators

6.N.2 Define and identify the commutative and associative properties of addition and multiplication

6.N.4 Define and identify the identity and inverse properties of addition and multiplication

6.N.3 Define and identify the distributive property of multiplication over addition

6.N.5 Define and identify the zero property of multiplication

6.R.9 Use mathematics to show and understand mathematical phenomena (i.e., Find the missing value: $(3 + 4) + 5 = 3 + (4 + \_\_)$)

VOCABULARY

The **Commutative Properties of Addition and Multiplication** state that the order in which two numbers are added or multiplied does not change the sum or product.

The **Associative Properties of Addition and Multiplication** state that the grouping of the addends or factors does not change the sum or products.

The **Identity Properties of Addition and Multiplication** state that if you add a number to 0, the sum is the same as the given number, and if you multiply a number by 1, the product is the same as the given number.

The **Inverse Properties of Addition and Multiplication** are properties that involve operations that undo each other. Addition and subtraction are inverse operations, and multiplication and division are inverse operations.

The **Distributive Property of Multiplication over Addition** states that to multiply a sum by a number, you can multiply each addend by the same number and add the products.

The **Zero Property of Multiplication** states any number multiplied by zero is zero.

REVIEW

Understanding Properties

The properties of addition and multiplication can easily be identified by certain main ideas.

The commutative properties deal with *order*, for example, $6 + 9 = 9 + 6$ or $6 \times 9 = 9 \times 6$.

The associative properties deal with *grouping*, for example, $5 + (2 + 6) = (5 + 2) + 6$ or $5 \times (2 \times 6) = (5 \times 2) \times 6$.

Applying Properties

Properties of numbers can also help you find missing terms and factors.

Example

Your teacher writes $1 \times 46 = \_\_$ on the board and asks the class to give the missing number and identify the property shown by the mathematical sentence.

The missing number is 46. The property shown is the Identity Property of Multiplication.

Identifying Properties

You may have to write or fill in a missing term in a mathematical sentence in order to identify the property used. Compare the two sides of the sentence to see which of the properties it shows. Use the key idea of each property to help you.

EXAMPLE 1

Cassie and Daniel are both reading the same book. One day Cassie reads 18 pages, and Daniel reads 23 pages. The next day Cassie reads 23 pages, and Daniel reads 18 pages. Identify the property used in the problem.

You can solve this problem by writing a mathematical sentence to represent the property. Write a mathematical sentence that shows the number of pages that each reads.

$$\text{Cassie: } 18 + 23 = 41 \qquad \text{Daniel: } 23 + 18 = 41$$

Write a mathematical sentence that shows these quantities are equal.

$$18 + 23 = 23 + 18$$

Think: Which property says the order in which two numbers are added doesn't change the sum?

Commutative Property of Addition

▶ **Understanding the Solution** The mathematical sentence shows both students read the same number of pages, 41. Since they read the same total number of pages but in a different order, the Commutative Property of Addition is shown.

TRY IT!

A sixth grade football team scored 21 points during the first half of their football game and no points during the second half of the game. Identify the property used in the problem.

EXAMPLE 2

Your teacher writes this number sentence on the board. Find the missing factor and identify the property.

$$(5 \times 3) \times 6 = 5 \times (\_\_ \times 6)$$

You can solve this problem by filling in the missing factor in the sentence. The numbers on the left are 5, 3, 6 and on the right are 5, ?, 6.

Think: What number is missing?

$$(5 \times 3) \times 6 = 5 \times (3 \times 6)$$

The parentheses are used for grouping. The factors within the parentheses have changed from side to side.

Think: Which property changes the grouping?

Associative Property of Multiplication

▶ **Understanding the Solution**   The numbers are still in the same order, which means the missing number has to be 3. The parentheses are not around the same numbers, so the grouping has changed, indicating the Associative Property of Multiplication.

TRY IT!

The problem $78 \times \underline{} = 0$ appeared on a test. What number makes this true? Identify the property shown by the problem.

EXAMPLE 3

Pat needed to find the product 8 × 17. She decided to use one of the properties. She wrote 8 × (10 + 7) = (8 × 10) + (__ × __) on her paper. Find the missing numbers. What property did she use?

You can solve this problem by filling in the missing numbers.
The right side needs to show 8 times each of the addends of 10 and 7. You have 8×10. What is missing?

$$8 \times 7$$

What property says multiplying a sum by a number is the same as multiplying the same number times the addends and adding the products?

Distributive Property of Multiplication over Addition

▶ **Understanding the Solution** $8 \times (10 + 7)$ shows the sum, $10 + 7$, multiplied by the number 8. $(8 \times 10) + (8 \times 7)$ shows the number 8 times each of the addends. These two expressions are equal to each other and are examples of the Distributive Property of Multiplication over Addition.

TRY IT!

What operation undoes adding 5 to a number? How do you know?

Exercises

1 Rick writes the problem $6 \times (20 + 8)$ on his paper. Amanda writes the problem $(6 \times 20) + (6 \times 8)$ on her paper. What property states that these two expressions are equal? Write the mathematical sentence that defines this property.

Show your work.

Answer _____

_____

MULTIPLE CHOICE

2 Which mathematical sentence correctly shows the Identity Property of Addition?

A $23 + 10 = 10 + 23$

B $0 + 45 = 45$

C $4 + 7 = 12, 12 - 7 = 4$

D $5 + 1 = 6$

3 Stacy wrote $78 + (69 + 32) = (78 + 69) + 32$ on her paper in order to show one of the properties. Which property is shown?

A Inverse Property of Addition

B Identity Property of Addition

C Commutative Property of Addition

D Associative Property of Addition

4 Which mathematical sentence represents the Distributive Property of Multiplication over Addition?

A $12 + (6 \times 11) = (12 + 6) \times (12 + 11)$

B $12 \times (6 \times 11) = (12 \times 6) + (12 \times 11)$

C $12 \times (6 + 11) = (12 \times 6) + (12 \times 11)$

D $12 \times (6 + 11) = (12 \times 6) + (12)$

5 Give the number and identify the property that makes this mathematical sentence true.

$67 + \underline{} = 38 + 67$

A 38; Commutative Property of Addition

B 105; Associative Property of Addition

C 38; Associative Property of Addition

D 38; Inverse Property of Addition

6 Tim needs to write a mathematical sentence that will show the Identity Property of Multiplication. Which sentence should he write?

A $4 \times 6 = 6 \times 4$

B $88 \times 0 = 0$

C $75 \times 1 = 75$

D $69 + 0 = 69$

7 Identify the property shown by $93 \times (56 \times 34) = 93 \times (34 \times 56)$.

A Associative Property of Multiplication

B Commutative Property of Multiplication

C Distributive Property of Multiplication over Addition

D Associative Property of Addition

8 Robert needed to find the answer to the problem 7×37. He knew he could use a property to help him. He wrote $7 \times (30 + 7) = $ _____. His little sister erased the right side of the mathematical sentence. What did she erase?

Part A

What property should he use? How do you know?

Show your work.

Answer _____
_____
_____

Part B

Fill in the blank to complete the property he was using.

Show your work.

Answer _____

LESSON 4.3 — Problem-Solving Strategy: Making a Table

New York Performance Indicators

6.PS.15 Make organized lists or charts to solve numerical problems

6.PS.21 Explain the methods and reasoning behind the problem solving strategies used

Understand the Strategy

Some problems can be solved by putting the data in a table or chart. Tables allow you to organize and display your data into columns and rows with labels in order to solve your problem. They are especially useful when you have two sets of data that are occurring at the same time but at different rates.

Problem: Casey collects baseball and football cards. For every 4 football cards she collects, she collects 9 baseball cards. How many baseball cards will she have if she collects 28 football cards?

SOLUTION

What do you know?

4 football cards for every 9 baseball cards

Number of football cards = 28

What do you need to find?

Number of baseball cards she has

Find the relationship.

You can use a table to help you organize what you know. Begin by making a table with the headings *Baseball* and *Football*. You know that if Casey has 4 football cards, she must have 9 baseball cards.

Football	4						
Baseball	9						

Since the number of football cards increases in groups of 4, you can fill in the top row of the table: 4, 8, 12, 16, etc. Similar reasoning can be used to fill in the bottom row: 9, 18, 27, etc.

Football	4	8	12	16	20	24	28
Baseball	9	18	27	36	45	54	63

So Casey has 63 baseball cards.

▶ **Understanding the Solution** Does your answer make sense? Since the number of football cards, 4, is multiplied by 7 to get 28, the number of baseball cards, 9, should also be multiplied by 7. Since $9 \times 7 = 63$, 63 baseball cards make sense.

1 Jordan and Tao go jogging each week. For every 2 miles Jordan jogs in a week, Tao jogs 7 miles. Jordan jogs 26 miles. How many miles will Tao jog in the same period of time?

Show your work.

Answer _____

2 A school supply store sells pens and pencils. For every 8 pens they sell, 14 pencils are sold. The store sells 112 pencils. How many pens were sold?

Show your work.

Answer _____

LESSON 4.4   Ratios and Rates

New York Performance Indicators

6.N.6   Understand the concept of rate

6.N.7   Express equivalent ratios as a proportion

6.N.8   Distinguish between rate and ratio

6.PS.7   Represent problem situations verbally, numerically, algebraically, and/or graphically

6.PS.23 Verify results of a problem

VOCABULARY

A **ratio** is a comparison of two quantities by division.

A **rate** is a ratio that compares two quantities with different kinds of units.

A **proportion** is an equation stating that two ratios or rates are equivalent.

Equivalent ratios are ratios that can be represented by equivalent fractions.

REVIEW

Understanding Ratios

A ratio uses division to compare two amounts or quantities. Write a ratio that compares 8 girls in a class to the 10 boys in a class. This ratio of the number of girls to the number of boys can be written three ways:

- using a colon $8:10$
- using the word "to"   8 to 10
- using a fraction $\frac{8}{10}$

Usually ratios are expressed as fractions in simplest form. You can simplify the ratio $\frac{8}{10}$ as $\frac{4}{5}$. Since the two ratios are equivalent, the equation $\frac{8}{10} = \frac{4}{5}$ is a proportion.

Applying Ratios

A school parking lot contains 35 cars and 9 trucks. What is the ratio of trucks to the number of vehicles on the lot?

There are a total of 44 vehicles on the lot.

So the ratio of trucks to vehicles is $\frac{9}{44}$.

Rates

Rates are ratios that compare different kinds of units such as miles to gallons. A rate that can be simplified so the denominator becomes 1 is called a unit rate. The denominator of the rate may have to be multiplied or divided by a number in order to change it to 1. The numerator must be multiplied or divided by the same number as the denominator, in order to keep the two rates equivalent.

EXAMPLE 1

One day in typing class, Duncan typed 115 words in 5 minutes. How many words per minute did he type?

You can solve this problem by finding the unit rate.

Write a rate comparing the number of words to the number of minutes.

$$\frac{115 \text{ words}}{5 \text{ minutes}}$$

Divide both the numerator and denominator by 5 in order to obtain the unit rate.

$$\frac{115 \text{ words} \div 5}{5 \text{ minutes} \div 5} = \frac{23 \text{ words}}{1 \text{ minute}}$$

▶ **Understanding the Solution**   A unit rate of $\frac{23 \text{ words}}{1 \text{ minute}}$ means that Duncan can type 23 words in one minute or 23 words per minute.

TRY IT!

A car travels 72 miles and uses 4 gallons of gasoline. How many miles per gallon does the car get?

Proportions

Two ratios or rates form a proportion if they can be shown to be equivalent. There are several ways to show that two ratios or rates are proportional.

- One way is to change each rate or ratio to a fraction using their least common denominator (LCD). If these fractions are the same, the original ratios or rates are proportional.
- Another way is to show that the ratios or rates are equivalent to each other. The ratios or rates are equivalent to each other if both the numerator and denominator of one can be multiplied or divided by the same number to obtain the other.
- A third way is to show that the two fractions are each equivalent to the same unit rate.

EXAMPLE 2

One day 12 people entered Store A in 15 minutes. At Store B, 8 people entered in 10 minutes. Are the rates at which people entered these stores proportional? Explain. If proportional, write the proportion.

You can solve this problem by changing the rates to fractions using their LCD.

Write a rate for each set of quantities that compares people to minutes.

$$\frac{12 \text{ people}}{15 \text{ minutes}} \qquad \frac{8 \text{ people}}{10 \text{ minutes}}$$

The LCD for 15 and 10 is 30. Change each rate to a fraction with a denominator of 30.

$$\frac{12}{15} = \frac{12 \times 2}{15 \times 2} = \frac{24}{30} \qquad \frac{8}{10} = \frac{8 \times 3}{10 \times 3} = \frac{24}{30}$$

Yes, since $\frac{12}{15} = \frac{24}{30}$ and $\frac{8}{10} = \frac{24}{30}$ the rates are proportional. So $\frac{12 \text{ people}}{15 \text{ minutes}} = \frac{8 \text{ people}}{10 \text{ minutes}}$.

▶ **Understanding the Solution**   Since the two unit rates are both equivalent to the same fraction, the rates are proportional.

TRY IT!

Doctor A sees 84 patients in 7 days. Doctor B sees 60 patients in 5 days. Are these patients per day rates proportional? Explain. Write the proportion if they are proportional.

EXAMPLE 3

Ryan's team won 3 games out of the 5 games they played. Pete's team won 12 games out of the 20 games they played. Are the two rates proportional? Explain. If proportional, write the proportion.

You can solve this problem by determining if the two quantities are equivalent to each other.

Write each quantity as a ratio.

$$\frac{3 \text{ games won}}{5 \text{ games played}} \qquad \frac{12 \text{ games won}}{20 \text{ games played}}$$

Multiply by the numerator and denominator of the fraction $\frac{3}{5}$ by 4.

$$\frac{3 \times 4}{5 \times 4} = \frac{12}{20}$$

Yes, the first ratio is equivalent to the second ratio.

$$\text{So } \frac{3 \text{ games won}}{5 \text{ games played}} = \frac{12 \text{ games won}}{20 \text{ games played}}.$$

▶ **Understanding the Solution**   Since both the numerator and denominator of the first fraction can be multiplied by 4 to get the second ratio, the fractions are equivalent.

$$\frac{3 \text{ games won}}{5 \text{ games played}} = \frac{12 \text{ games won}}{20 \text{ games played}}$$

TRY IT!

Hillary paid $4 for 6 paperback books. Allison paid $10 for 12 books. Are these two rates proportional? Explain. If proportional, write the proportion.

Exercises

SHORT RESPONSE

1 In Ms. Perkin's class there are 12 boys and 14 girls. In Mr. Twig's class there are 10 boys and 16 girls. The two classes are combined for a field trip. What is the new ratio of boys to girls? Give the answer in simplest form.

Show your work.

Answer _____

MULTIPLE CHOICE

2 Which of the following is <u>not</u> proportional to $\frac{48}{64}$?

A $\frac{6}{8}$

B $\frac{24}{32}$

C $\frac{3}{4}$

D $\frac{2}{3}$

3 A bookcase holds 12 mystery books, 24 science fiction books, and 32 fiction books. What is the ratio of science fiction books to the number of books on the bookcase, written in simplest form?

A 6 to 17

B 3 to 17

C 8 to 17

D 17 to 8

4 Which of the following represents a pair of proportional ratios or rates?

A 3 hits in 5 times at bat; 6 hits in 15 times at bat

B 16 steps in 2 minutes; 24 steps in 4 minutes

C $81 for 3 baseball tickets; $54 for 2 baseball tickets

D 183 miles driven in 3 hours; 248 miles in 4 hours

5 The ratio of black squares to white squares in a design is 5 to 6. Which of these shows possible numbers of black and white squares?

A 25 black, 36 white

B 50 black, 66 white

C 40 black, 48 white

D 20 black, 21 white

6 While on a six-day vacation, the Johnson family spent $984. How much did they spend per day?

A $328 per day

B $164 per day

C $161 per day

D $114 per day

7 Which of the following represents a rate?

A 680 miles in 3 days

B 34 red beads to 8 white beads

C 54 students to 3 teachers

D 180 days to 20 weeks

8 Mrs. Ashby needs 7 rolls of wallpaper to paper a room. The store sells the wallpaper she wants for $6.98 a roll or 2 rolls for $10.95. What is the cost per roll for buying 7 rolls?

Show your work.

Answer _____

9 Jonelle is making a bracelet with red and yellow beads. She alternates 2 red beads with 5 yellow beads. If she needs 16 red beads to complete a bracelet, how many yellow beads does she need?

Show your work.

Answer _____

LESSON 4.5 Solving Proportions

New York Performance Indicators

6.N.9 Solve proportions using equivalent fractions

6.N.10 Verify the proportionality using the product of the means equals the product of the extremes

6.PS.8 Select an appropriate representation of a problem

6.PS.7 Represent problem situations verbally, numerically, algebraically, and/or graphically

6.PS.23 Verify results of a problem

VOCABULARY

In the proportion $\frac{a}{b} = \frac{c}{d}$, the **extreme terms** (or **extremes**) are a and d. The **mean terms** (or **means**) are b and c.

REVIEW

Understanding Proportions

A proportion is an equation stating that two ratios or rates are equivalent.

$$\frac{12}{30} = \frac{2}{5}$$

You can verify that these two ratios are equivalent by checking to see if the product of the means (30×2) is equal to the product of the extremes (12×5). If the products are equal, then the two ratios are proportional.

$$30 \times 2 = 60 \text{ and } 12 \times 5 = 60$$

So the ratios are proportional.

Applying Proportions

Do the two ratios $\frac{3}{5}$ and $\frac{24}{40}$ form a proportion?

Verify that they do by checking to see if the product of the means and the product of the extremes are equal.

Means: $5 \times 24 = 120$
Extremes: $3 \times 40 = 120$

The ratios form the proportion $\frac{3}{5} = \frac{24}{40}$.

Verifying the Proportionality of a Proportion

You can verify or check the proportionality of a proportion using the product of the means equals the product of the extremes. If the two products are equal, then the two fractions form a proportion.

EXAMPLE 1

Is $\frac{6}{8} = \frac{9}{12}$ a proportion?

You can solve this problem by verifying the proportionality of the proportion.

To verify or check to see if you have a true proportion, find the product of the means and the product of the extremes. If these two products are equal, then the two fractions are equivalent.

Means: $8 \times 9 = 72$　　　Extremes: $6 \times 12 = 72$

Yes, $\frac{6}{8} = \frac{9}{12}$ is a proportion.

▶ **Understanding the Solution**　The means and the extremes both have the same product of 72. Since the products are equal, the fractions are equivalent. So, $\frac{6}{8} = \frac{9}{12}$ is a proportion. You have verified the proportionality of the proportions.

TRY IT!

Is $\frac{49}{56} = \frac{21}{27}$ a proportion? Explain.

Solving a Proportion

A proportion can be solved by finding the unknown value in the proportion. Once found, the unknown value makes the fractions equivalent. Equivalent fractions can be found by multiplying or dividing both the numerator and denominator of one fraction by the same number in order to get the other fraction. Use the relationship between either the two denominators or the two numerators to determine whether to multiply or divide. If there isn't any easily seen relationship, then simplify the ratio and work with an equivalent fraction.

EXAMPLE 2

Solve the proportion $\frac{28}{36} = \frac{14}{y}$. Then verify the proportionality.

You can solve this problem by solving the proportion.

To find the value of y, use the relationship between the two numerators, 28 and 14. Since $28 \div 2 = 14$, divide both the numerator and denominator of the fraction $\frac{28}{36}$ by 2.

$$y = 36 \div 2$$
$$y = 18$$

Use the means and extremes to verify that $\frac{28}{36} = \frac{14}{18}$ is a proportion.

Means: $36 \times 14 = 504$　　　Extremes: $28 \times 18 = 504$

▶ **Understanding the Solution**　You have solved the proportion by finding $y = 18$. By showing that the product of the means and the product of the extremes are both equal to 504, you have verified that the missing value, 18, makes $\frac{28}{36} = \frac{14}{18}$ a proportion.

TRY IT!

Solve the proportion $\frac{w}{9} = \frac{30}{54}$. Then verify the proportionality.

EXAMPLE 3

In a class of 24 sixth graders, 14 of the students say they have cell phones. There are 60 sixth graders in the school. If the ratio remains the same, how many sixth graders in the school have a cell phone?

You can solve this problem by writing and solving a proportion.

Write a proportion to represent the situation. Let m = the number of sixth graders in the school with cell phones. Set a proportion:

$$\frac{14}{24} = \frac{m}{60}$$

Since the relationship between 24 and 60 cannot easily be related by multiplication or division, simplify the ratio of $\frac{14}{24}$ by dividing both the numerator and denominator by 2. $\frac{14}{24}$ is equivalent to $\frac{7}{12}$.

$$\frac{7}{12} = \frac{m}{60}$$

Then solve using $5 \times 12 = 60$. Multiply both 7 and 12 by 5.

$$m = 7 \times 5$$
$$m = 35 \text{ cell phones}$$

▶ **Understanding the Solution**   You can check to see that you have the correct answer by verifying the proportionality of $\frac{14}{24} = \frac{35}{60}$. Since the product of the means, 24×35, is 840 and the product of the extremes, 14×60, is 840, you know the two fractions are equivalent and that you have correctly solved the problem.

TRY IT!

Kate has a job working at a banquet center. One week she worked 12 hours and earned $96. How much will she earn if she works 9 hours?

Exercises

SHORT RESPONSE

1 In a survey of 50 people, 10 people said they watched less than 5 hours of TV per week. If the ratio stayed the same, how many people would have been surveyed if 15 people said they watched less than 5 hours of TV per week?

Show your work.

Answer _____

2 Which pair of ratios can be verified as a proportion by using the product of their means and extremes?

A $\frac{18}{24}, \frac{27}{32}$

B $\frac{10}{12}, \frac{35}{42}$

C $\frac{16}{30}, \frac{24}{75}$

D $\frac{8}{20}, \frac{14}{30}$

3 Emma runs for 18 minutes out of the 45 minutes she spends exercising each morning. One morning she spends 70 minutes exercising. If her rate stays the same, how many minutes will she spend running?

A 24 minutes

B 30 minutes

C 25 minutes

D 28 minutes

4 A store has 13-ounce bags of chips on sale. You can buy 4 bags for $10 during the sale. Which proportion can be used to find the number of bags of chips that can be bought for $15?

A $\frac{4}{10} = \frac{c}{15}$

B $\frac{4}{c} = \frac{15}{10}$

C $\frac{4}{13} = \frac{c}{15}$

D $\frac{4}{10} = \frac{15}{c}$

5 Solve the following proportion.

$\frac{9}{y} = \frac{14}{42}$

A 18

B 26

C 27

D 28

6 Which of the following is not a proportion?

A $\frac{4}{5} = \frac{36}{45}$

B $\frac{6}{15} = \frac{40}{100}$

C $\frac{1}{2} = \frac{17}{35}$

D $\frac{8}{3} = \frac{128}{48}$

7 Karen gets 6 out of every 8 questions on a test correct. If she gets 27 questions correct, how many questions are on the test?

A 36 questions

B 42 questions

C 48 questions

D 33 questions

8 Solve the following proportion.

$\frac{12}{15} = \frac{x}{45}$

A 3

B 5

C 24

D 36

9 An electronic store had a sale on CDs and DVDs. For every 8 CDs sold, there were 12 DVDs sold. There was a combined total of 70 CDs and DVDs sold one day. If the rate stayed the same, how many CDs were sold that day?

Part A

Write a proportion to show the relationship and solve it to find the number of CDs sold.
Show your work.

Answer _____

Part B

Verify the proportionality of the proportion you used.
Show your work.

Answer _____

LESSON 4.6 Understanding Percents

 New York Performance Indicators

6.N.11 Read, write and identify percents of a whole (0% to 100%)

6.PS.7 Represent problem situations verbally, numerically, algebraically, and/or graphically

6.PS.5 Formulate problems and solutions from everyday situations

VOCABULARY

A **percent** is the ratio of a part of a whole divided into hundredths to 100.

REVIEW

Understanding Percents

To show that a number is a percent, use the symbol %. Since a percent is part of 100, it can be written as a ratio.

6% means 6 out of 100 or $\frac{6}{100}$.

Ratios can be changed to percents by solving a proportion. To change 7 out of 50 to a percent, write and solve a proportion.

$$\frac{7}{50} = \frac{x}{100}$$

$$\frac{7}{50} = \frac{14}{100}$$

$$x = 14$$

So 7 out of 50 is equal to 14%

Applying Percents

Evan was making a design that used red and blue square tiles. If 3 out of 10 tiles were red, what percent of the tiles were red?

$$\frac{3}{10} = \frac{x}{100}$$

$$\frac{3}{10} = \frac{30}{100}$$

$$x = 30$$

So, 30% of the tiles were red.

Finding Percents

You can find a percent by writing a proportion. Use $\frac{x}{100}$ to represent the missing percent. Set the ratio from the problem equal to $\frac{x}{100}$ and solve using equivalent fractions. The amount out of 100 is the percent.

EXAMPLE 1

What percent is 1 out of 20?

You can solve this problem by writing and solving a proportion.

Write a proportion using the ratio as a fraction equal to $\frac{x}{100}$.

$$\frac{1}{20} = \frac{x}{100}$$

Solve the proportion using equivalent fractions. Change $\frac{1}{20}$ to an equivalent fraction with a denominator of 100.

$$\frac{1}{20} = \frac{5}{100}$$

The number out of 100 is the percent.

So, 1 out of 20 is 5%.

▶ **Understanding the Solution**   The ratio of 1 out of 20 is equivalent to 5 out of 100. Since every percent is out of 100, 1 out of 20 is 5%. Be sure to include the % sign in your answer.

TRY IT!

What percent is 8 out of 25?

EXAMPLE 2

A professional baseball team has 25 players on its roster from Opening Day to August 31. If 6 of the players are left-handed batters, what percent of the players on the roster are left-handed batters?

You can solve this problem by writing and solving a proportion.
Write a proportion using the ratio 6 out of 25.

$$\frac{6}{25} = \frac{x}{100}$$

Change $\frac{6}{25}$ to an equivalent fraction with a denominator of 100.

$$\frac{6}{25} = \frac{24}{100}$$

$$x = 24$$

So 24% of the players are left-handed batters.

▶ **Understanding the Solution**   In order to find a percent equivalent to $\frac{6}{25}$, change $\frac{6}{25}$ to an equivalent fraction whose denominator is 100. Since $\frac{6}{25} = \frac{24}{100}$, 6 out of 25 is 24%.

TRY IT!

Ethan has a collection of 50 DVDs. If 32 of the DVDs are comedies, what percent of the DVDs are comedies?

EXAMPLE 3

A sixth grade class conducted a survey. They asked 40 of their friends how many of them had a pet. The survey showed that 18 of their friends had pets. What percent of their friends had a pet?

You can solve this problem by writing and solving a proportion.

Use the ratio 18 out of 40 to write the proportion.

$$\frac{18}{40} = \frac{x}{100}$$

The denominator 40 isn't easily related by multiplication or division to 100. Simplify $\frac{18}{40}$ by dividing both numerator and denominator by 2.

$$\frac{18}{40} = \frac{9}{20}$$

Change $\frac{9}{20}$ to an equivalent fraction whose denominator is 100.

$$\frac{9}{20} = \frac{45}{100}$$

$$x = 45$$

So, 45% had a pet.

▶ **Understanding the Solution** The fraction $\frac{18}{40}$ doesn't change easily to a fraction with a denominator of 100. It has to be simplified to $\frac{9}{20}$ and then changed to an equivalent fraction whose denominator is 100. The fraction $\frac{45}{100}$ gives the percent, so 18 out of 40 is 45%.

TRY IT!

Records were kept at an airport concerning whether the flights leaving the airport were full or had available seats on the plane. One morning 80 flights left the airport. There were 16 flights that left the airport with available seats on the planes. What percent of the flights leaving the airport had available seats?

Exercises

1 Nikki works as a cashier at the ABC Grocery Store. One day she checked out 36 people. Of the people she checked out, 9 were men. What percent of the people checked out were men?

Show your work.

Answer _____

MULTIPLE CHOICE

2 Which of the following is the same as 58%?

A $\frac{58}{10}$

B $\frac{29}{10}$

C $\frac{58}{100}$

D $\frac{29}{100}$

3 Kevin was watching a DVD that was 125 minutes long. A friend called, and he talked to his friend for 15 minutes while the DVD was playing. What percent of the length of time of the DVD did he spend talking to his friend on his phone?

A 12%

B 15%

C 25%

D 3%

4 A parking garage has 500 parking spaces. One morning 330 parking spots were filled. What percent of the parking spaces were filled?

A 330%

B 33%

C 10%

D 66%

5 Which percent is equivalent to 8 out of 10?

A 8%

B 80%

C 800%

D 16%

6 At a school there are 63 sixth grade students who buy their lunch. There are 90 students in the sixth grade. What percent of the sixth grade students in the school buy their lunch?

A 70%

B 63%

C 90%

D 10%

7 Peter spends $75 for a video game and a CD. The CD costs $15. The cost of the CD is what percent of the money spent on the game and CD?

A 1%

B 5%

C 15%

D 20%

8 Jackie wants to buy a digital camera that sells for $250. She has $120 saved.

Part A

What percent of the camera's price has she saved?

Show your work.

Answer _____

Part B

She finds the camera on sale for $200. What percent of the sale price does she have saved?

Show your work.

Answer _____

LESSON 4.7   Solving Percent Problems

New York Performance Indicators

6.N.12 Solve percent problems involving percent, rate, and base

6.PS.7 Represent problem situations verbally, numerically, algebraically, and/or graphically

6.PS.5 Formulate problems and solutions from everyday situations

VOCABULARY

In a percent problem, the **base** is the original or whole amount that the part is being compared to.

The **part** is the amount being compared to the whole amount.

REVIEW

Understanding Percent Problems

To understand the parts of a percent problem, look at the problem below.

What number is 30% of 50?

The percent (rate) is 30% or 30 out of 100. The 50 is the base because it is the whole amount. The part, the amount compared to 50, is missing.

To find the part, you can use the two ratios, 30 out of 100 and a number out of 50, to write a proportion.

$$\frac{x}{50} = \frac{30}{100}$$

Use equivalent fractions to solve the proportion.

$$\frac{x}{50} = \frac{30 \div 2}{100 \div 2}$$

$$\frac{x}{50} = \frac{15}{50}$$

$$x = 15$$

So 30% of 50 is 15.

Applying Percent Problems

Jon had 90% of the 40 questions on a math test correct. Write a proportion that could be used to find the number of questions Jon had correct on the test.

$$\frac{x}{40} = \frac{90}{100}$$

To solve the proportion, simplify $\frac{90}{100}$.

$$\frac{x}{40} = \frac{9}{10}$$

$$\frac{x}{40} = \frac{9 \times 4}{10 \times 4}$$

$$\frac{x}{40} = \frac{36}{40}$$

$$x = 36$$

So Jon had 36 problems on his test correct.

Solving Percent Problems

You can use the proportion $\frac{\text{part}}{\text{base}} = \frac{\text{percent}}{100}$ to find any one of the missing terms in a percent problem. The proportion can be solved using equivalent fractions.

EXAMPLE 1

In one sixth grade class, 75% of the 24 students in the class have at least one brother or sister. How many students have at least one brother or sister?

You can solve this problem by writing and solving a proportion.

The percent is 75%. The number 24 represents the base—all of the students in the class. So the part is missing. Use this information and the proportion $\frac{\text{part}}{\text{base}} = \frac{\text{percent}}{100}$ to write a proportion.

$$\frac{x}{24} = \frac{75}{100}$$

Solve the proportion using equivalent fractions. Divide both 75 and 100 by 25 to get $\frac{3}{4}$.

$$\frac{x}{24} = \frac{3}{4}$$

Multiply 3 and 4 by 6 to get an equivalent fraction, $\frac{18}{24}$.

$$\frac{x}{24} = \frac{18}{24}$$

$$x = 18$$

Understanding the Solution   If 18 out of 24 students have a brother or sister, is that 75%? You know that $\frac{18}{24} = \frac{3}{4}$, and if both 3 and 4 are multiplied by 25, the resulting ratio is $\frac{75}{100}$, or 75%.

TRY IT!

When asked if they had ever visited the Statue of Liberty, 65% of the 120 people asked said that they had. How many people said they had visited the Statue of Liberty?

EXAMPLE 2

One day 400 students bought their lunch in the school cafeteria. The students buying their lunch were 80% of the students in the school. How many students attend the school?

You can solve this problem by writing and solving a proportion.

The percent is 80%. Since not all of the students bought their lunch, the 400 must be the part. So, the base is missing. Write a proportion using $\frac{\text{part}}{\text{base}} = \frac{\text{percent}}{100}$.

$$\frac{400}{x} = \frac{80}{100}$$

Multiply 80 and 100 by 5 to get an equivalent fraction $\frac{400}{500}$.

$$\frac{400}{x} = \frac{400}{500}$$

$$x = 500$$

▶ **Understanding the Solution**   The 500 represents all of the students in the school. 400 out of 500 is equivalent to $\frac{80}{100}$, or 80%.

TRY IT!

Mr. Jordan planted 16 tomato plants in his garden along with other vegetable plants. The tomato plants were 64% of the vegetable plants in his garden. How many vegetable plants were in his garden?

Exercises

SHORT RESPONSE

1 Matt has a part-time job at an automotive store. He earns $140 a week and spends 35% of the money he earns on clothes. How much does he spend on clothes?

Show your work.

Answer _____

2 What number is 88% of 175?

  A 199
  B 154
  C 200
  D 132

5 98 is 14% of what number?

  A 280
  B 700
  C 600
  D 199

3 In Centerville during the month of February, the sun didn't shine on 75% of the 28 days. How many days didn't the sun shine?

  A 7 days
  B 14 days
  C 20 days
  D 21 days

6 Adam likes to do crossword puzzles. He has a book of 200 puzzles. He has finished 95% of the puzzles in the book. How many puzzles has he finished?

  A 180 puzzles
  B 175 puzzles
  C 190 puzzles
  D 195 puzzles

4 Of a group of 25 sixth graders, 40% of them said they had never visited another state. How many students said they had never visited another state?

  A 10 students
  B 15 students
  C 12 students
  D 11 students

7 People leaving an ice cream store were asked to name their favorite flavor of ice cream. Fifty-one people said chocolate was their favorite flavor. If 68% of the people surveyed said chocolate, how many people were surveyed?

  A 75 people
  B 34 people
  C 17 people
  D 104 people

8 Mrs. Hsu bought 40 items at the bakery to take to the school where she teaches. Of the items bought, 60% were bagels.

Part A

How many bagels did she buy?

Show your work.

Answer _____

Part B

If 25% of the bagels were plain, how many plain bagels did she buy?

Show your work.

Answer _____

LESSON 4.8 Problem-Solving Strategy: Finding a Pattern

New York Performance Indicators
6.PS.14 Analyze problems by observing patterns

Understand the Strategy

Some problems can be solved by finding a pattern that causes each term in the pattern to change in a predictable way. To identify the rule for a pattern, ask yourself what happens to the first term to get the second term, to get the third term, and each term after that. A pattern can be numeric, dealing with numbers, or geometric, dealing with designs.

Problem: One day a class put 3 pennies in a jar as part of an experiment. The next day the students put 6 pennies in the jar. On the third day 12 pennies went into the jar. And on the fourth day 24 pennies went into the jar. If the pattern continues, how many pennies will they put in the jar on the eighth day?

SOLUTION

What do you know?

3 pennies first day

6 pennies second day

12 pennies third day

24 pennies fourth day

What do you need to find?

Number of pennies on eighth day

Find the relationship.

You know the number of pennies going into the jar for four days: 3, 6, 12, 24. What is happening to each number to get the next number? The pattern shows the previous number being doubled, or multiplied by 2, to get the next number.

Day 1: 3 pennies

Day 2: $2 \times 3 = 6$ pennies

Day 3: $2 \times 6 = 12$ pennies

Day 4: $2 \times 12 = 24$ pennies

Day 5: $2 \times 24 = 48$ pennies

Day 6: $2 \times 48 = 96$ pennies

Day 7: $2 \times 96 = 192$ pennies

Day 8: $2 \times 192 = 384$ pennies

So the class will put 384 pennies in the jar on the eighth day.

▶ Understanding the Solution Since the rule for finding the pattern is to multiply by 2, you could check your result by dividing the number of pennies each day by 2 to see if you get the previous day's number of pennies until you get back to 3 pennies.

1 A sixth grade teacher had the students in her class create number patterns. Tony came up with the following pattern. What do you think the next two numbers in Tony's pattern are?

$$4, 8, 7, 11, 10, 14, 13, 17, \underline{\quad}, \underline{\quad}$$

Show your work.

Answer _____

2 Draw the seventh figure in the pattern. How many dots will be in the drawing?

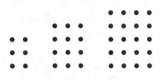

Show your work.

Answer _____

MULTIPLE CHOICE

1 Tom wrote the following group of letters on his paper. What percent of the letters are Bs?

AABBBBAABBAABBB

- **A** 40%
- **B** 60%
- **C** 20%
- **D** 55%

2 Which number correctly gives thirteen billion, five hundred sixty-three thousand, eighteen in standard form?

- **A** 13,000,563,018
- **B** 13,563,018
- **C** 13,563,000,018
- **D** 13,563,018,000

3 Which pair of ratios is proportional?

- **A** $\frac{18}{20}, \frac{34}{40}$
- **B** $\frac{5}{8}, \frac{25}{32}$
- **C** $\frac{24}{36}, \frac{18}{30}$
- **D** $\frac{22}{33}, \frac{18}{27}$

4 Identify the property shown by $6 \times (17 + 23) = (6 \times 17) + (6 \times 23)$.

- **A** Commutative Property of Multiplication
- **B** Associative Property of Addition
- **C** Inverse Property of Multiplication
- **D** Distributive Property of Multiplication over Addition

5 The net weight of 3 boxes of cereal is 54 ounces. Which proportion could be used to find the weight of 7 boxes?

- **A** $\frac{3}{7} = \frac{x}{54}$
- **B** $\frac{3}{54} = \frac{x}{7}$
- **C** $\frac{3}{54} = \frac{7}{x}$
- **D** $\frac{3}{x} = \frac{7}{54}$

6 Josh lifts weights for 5 minutes each day for one week. The second week he lifts weights for 8 minutes each day. The third week he lifts weights for 11 minutes each day. If the pattern continues, how many minutes will he lift weights each day during the eleventh week?

- **A** 32 minutes
- **B** 35 minutes
- **C** 38 minutes
- **D** 29 minutes

7 There were 500 tickets sold for Friday night's football game. The home team fans bought 350 tickets.

Part A

What percent of the tickets were sold to the home team fans?

Show your work.

Answer _____

Part B

If 60% of the 350 home team fans who bought tickets were students, how many students bought tickets?

Show your work.

Answer _____

8 Mitchell and Abby are saving part of their allowances each week. Mitchell is saving $2 per week. Abby is saving $3 per week. How much money will Abby have saved when Mitchell saves $16?

Show your work.

Answer _____

LESSON 5.1 Identifying and Ordering Rational Numbers

New York Performance Indicators

6.N.13 Define absolute value and determine the absolute value of rational numbers (including positive and negative)

6.N.14 Locate rational numbers on a number line (including positive and negative)

6.N.15 Order rational numbers (including positive and negative)

6.PS.13 Model problems with pictures/diagrams or physical objects

6.CN.5 Model situations with objects and representations and be able to draw conclusions

VOCABULARY

Absolute value is the distance between a number and zero on a number line. The absolute value of both −5 and 5 is the same, since both are the same distance from 0: $|5| = 5$, $|−5| = 5$.

A **rational number** is any number that can be written as a fraction of two whole numbers.

REVIEW

Understanding Rational Numbers

Rational numbers include integers, positive and negative decimals, fractions, and mixed numbers. Rational numbers can be represented on a number line.

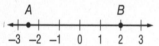

Point A is halfway between −2 and −3, so it could represent −2.5 or $−2\frac{1}{2}$. Point B represents 2.

What You Should Know

The value of numbers on a number line increases from left to right.

On the number line below, −1 is to the right of −3, so −1 is greater than −3. −3 is to the left of −1, so −3 is less than −1.

The order of the numbers represented on the number line from least to greatest is −3, −1, and 2.

Absolute Value

Look at −3 and 3 on the number line. −3 is three units from zero and 3 is three units from zero. Both have an absolute value of 3 because they are both three units from zero. The symbol for absolute value is $| \ |$.

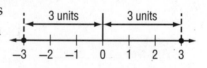

EXAMPLE 1

Evaluate $|−28| − |6|$.

You can solve this problem by writing an expression with the absolute values of −28 and 6 and then simplifying.

The absolute value of a number is its distance from 0 on the number line.

$$|−28| − |6| = 28 − 6$$
$$= 22$$

▶ **Understanding the Solution** Since distance cannot be less than zero, the absolute value of a number must be zero or greater than zero. $|-28| = 28$ since the absolute value of -28 is 28. $|6| = 6$ since the absolute value of 6 is 6. $28 - 6$ is 22.

TRY IT!

Evaluate $|-12| + |-15|$

Identifying and Ordering Rational Numbers

Number lines can be used to identify and order rational numbers. Since the value of numbers increases from left to right, numbers to the right of a number have a greater value, and numbers to the left of a number have a lesser value.

EXAMPLE 2

Which point on the number line is greater than -4 but less than 2?

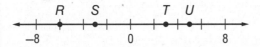

You can solve this problem by locating the point that lies between -4 and 2 on the number line.

Identify the interval between tick marks on the number line. Next identify the tick marks that represent -4 and 2. Then locate the point that lies between these two tick marks.

The interval between tick marks is 2. -4 on the number line is the second tick mark to the left of zero. 2 on the number line is the first tick mark to the right of zero.

The only point that lies between -4 and 2 is S, so S is the correct answer.

▶ **Understanding the Solution** The numbers represented by each point are: $R(-6)$, $S(-3)$, $T(3)$, and $U(5)$. R cannot be the point since -6 is located to the left of -4 and is less than -4. T and U cannot be the points since 3 and 5 are to the right of 2 and are greater than 2. S is the correct point since -3 is greater than -4 and less than 2.

TRY IT!

What point represents -1.2 on the number line?

```
     P   Q   R   S
  ◄──┼───┼───┼───┼───┼───►
    -2  -1   0   1   2
```

EXAMPLE 3

Andrea volunteers at the local animal shelter. She works $1\frac{1}{2}$ hours on Monday, $\frac{3}{4}$ hour on Tuesday, $1\frac{5}{6}$ hours on Wednesday, $\frac{2}{3}$ hour on Thursday, and $1\frac{1}{3}$ hours on Friday. List the times in order from least to greatest.

You can solve this problem by writing and comparing equivalent fractions.

The list of rational numbers you want to order are $1\frac{1}{2}, \frac{3}{4}, 1\frac{5}{6}, \frac{2}{3}, 1\frac{1}{3}$. The LCD of 2, 3, 4, and 6 is 12, so write equivalent fractions and mixed numbers with a denominator of 12.

Since you know that the fractions are less in value than the mixed numbers, write equivalent fractions for the fractions first.

$$\frac{3}{4} = \frac{3 \times 3}{4 \times 3} = \frac{9}{12} \text{ and } \frac{2}{3} = \frac{2 \times 4}{3 \times 4} = \frac{8}{12}$$

Since the whole numbers for $1\frac{1}{2}$, $1\frac{5}{6}$, and $1\frac{1}{3}$ are all 1, write equivalent fractions for the fraction part of the mixed numbers only.

$$1\frac{1}{2} = \frac{1 \times 6}{2 \times 6} = 1\frac{6}{12} \text{ and } 1\frac{5}{6} = \frac{5 \times 2}{6 \times 2} = 1\frac{10}{12} \text{ and } 1\frac{1}{3} = \frac{1 \times 4}{3 \times 4} = 1\frac{4}{12}$$

The fractions and mixed numbers you want to order are $\frac{9}{12}, \frac{8}{12}, 1\frac{6}{12}, 1\frac{10}{12}, 1\frac{4}{12}$

The denominators are the same, so use the numerators to order the numbers $\frac{8}{12}, \frac{9}{12}, 1\frac{4}{12}, 1\frac{6}{12}, 1\frac{10}{12} \rightarrow$ The times from least to greatest: $\frac{2}{3}, \frac{3}{4}, 1\frac{1}{3}, 1\frac{1}{2}, 1\frac{5}{6}$

▶ **Understanding the Solution**   You can also order the numbers by plotting them on a number line. Draw the number line from 0 to 2, divide it into twelfths, and then plot the numbers.

TRY IT!

Diego needs the following lengths of dowels for a project: $\frac{3}{4}$ inch, $1\frac{1}{4}$ inches, $\frac{5}{8}$ inch, $1\frac{3}{8}$ inches, and $\frac{1}{2}$ inch. What are the lengths of the dowels from shortest to longest?

Exercises

SHORT RESPONSE

1 Evaluate $|-18| + |-12|$.
Show your work.

Answer _____

MULTIPLE CHOICE

2 Maya is learning to scuba dive. The table shows the depth of her dives. Which list shows the dives in order from the shallowest to the deepest?

Dive	Depth (meters)
1	−1.55
2	−0.75
3	−1.6
4	−0.8
5	−1.7

A −1.7 −1.6 −1.55 −0.8 −0.75
B −1.7 −1.55 −1.6 −0.75 −0.8
C −0.8 −0.75 −1.6 −1.55 −1.7
D −0.75 −0.8 −1.55 −1.6 −1.7

3 Which letter represents $-\frac{5}{8}$ on the number line?

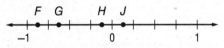

A F
B G
C H
D J

4 Which expression is equivalent to $|-22| + |6| + |-4|$?

A $22 + 6 + 4$
B $22 + 6 - 4$
C $-22 + 6 - 4$
D $-22 + 6 + 4$

5 Which number does R represent on the number line?

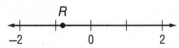

A −2.1
B −1.2
C −0.8
D −0.4

6 Which point on the number line is greater than −3 but less than 0?

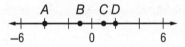

A A
B B
C C
D D

7 The weights listed on some spice packages are $\frac{2}{3}$ ounce, 0.625 ounce, $\frac{3}{8}$ ounce, and 0.65 ounce. Which list shows the weights in order from lightest to heaviest?

A $\frac{3}{8}$ 0.625 0.65 $\frac{2}{3}$

B $\frac{3}{8}$ 0.65 0.625 $\frac{2}{3}$

C $\frac{2}{3}$ 0.65 0.625 $\frac{3}{8}$

D $\frac{2}{3}$ 0.625 0.65 $\frac{3}{8}$

8 Dekentra is keeping a log of the miles she walks each day. So far, she walked $\frac{2}{3}$ mile on Saturday, $1\frac{3}{4}$ mile on Monday, $\frac{1}{2}$ mile on Tuesday, $2\frac{1}{8}$ mile on Wednesday, $1\frac{5}{8}$ mile on Thursday, and $\frac{5}{6}$ mile on Friday.

Part A

Plot the distances on the number line below. Label each point. Explain how you plotted the points.

Show your work.

```
   +--+--+--+--+--+--+--+--+--+--+--+--+--+--+
   0           1           2           3
```

Answer _____

_____

_____

_____

_____

_____

Part B

What is the order of the distances from shortest to longest distance? Explain how you used the number line to order the distances.

Show your work.

Answer _____

_____

_____

LESSON 5.2   Adding and Subtracting Fractions with Unlike Denominators

New York Performance Indicators

6.N.16 Add and subtract fractions with unlike denominators

6.PS.6 Translate from a picture/diagram to a numeric expression

6.PS.13 Model problems with pictures/diagrams or physical objects

VOCABULARY

The **Least Common Denominator (LCD)** is the least common multiple of the denominators of two or more fractions, used as a denominator.

Unlike fractions are fractions with different denominators.

A fraction is in **simplest form** when the numerator and the denominator have no common factor greater than 1.

REVIEW

Understanding Fractions with Unlike Denominators

You cannot add or subtract fractions with unlike denominators until you rename the fractions with a common denominator.

In a stack of T-shirts, $\frac{1}{8}$ are red and $\frac{3}{4}$ are blue. What fraction of the T-shirts are red or blue?

Rename $\frac{3}{4}$ as $\frac{6}{8}$ so that the fractions have the same denominator. Then add.

$$\frac{1}{8} + \frac{6}{8} = \frac{7}{8}$$

So, $\frac{7}{8}$ of the T-shirts are red or blue.

What You Should Know

You can find the least common multiple (LCM) of fractions by listing the multiples of the denominators, and then identifying the common multiples and the least common multiple.

Find the LCM of 4 and 6 to add $\frac{3}{4} + \frac{1}{6}$.

Multiples of 4: 4, 8, <u>12</u>, 16, 20, <u>24</u>, 28, 32

Multiples of 6: 6, <u>12</u>, 18, <u>24</u>, 36, 42, 48, 54

In these lists, the common multiples are 12 and 24, and the LCM is 12. Rename the fractions with the LCD as the common denominator.

$$\frac{3}{4} = \frac{9}{12} \text{ and } \frac{1}{6} = \frac{2}{12}$$

$$\frac{9}{12} + \frac{2}{12} = \frac{9+2}{12}$$

$$= \frac{11}{12}$$

Adding and Subtracting Fractions

You can use models to add and subtract fractions with unlike denominators, or you can find the LCD. Sums and differences should be written in simplest form.

EXAMPLE 1

In Mr. Nelson's sixth grade class, a poll of students shows that $\frac{1}{3}$ of the students voted for the Empire State Building as their favorite place to visit in New York City, and $\frac{2}{5}$ voted for the Statue of Liberty. What fraction of the students voted for the Empire State Building or the Statue of Liberty as their favorite place to visit in New York City?

You can solve this problem by using a model to add the fractions.

Shade one-third of the squares, or one row, to represent the students who voted for the Empire State Building. Shade 2 out of every 5 squares to represent the students who voted for the Statue of Liberty.

One-third of the squares or one row = 5 squares, so shade 5 squares.

Two out of every five squares = 6 squares, so shade 6 more squares.

The number of shaded squares represents the numerator of the fraction. The total number of squares represents the denominator of the fraction.

Since 11 out of 15 squares are shaded, the sum of $\frac{1}{3}$ and $\frac{2}{5}$ is $\frac{11}{15}$.

So, $\frac{11}{15}$ of the students voted for the Empire State Building or the Statue of Liberty.

Understanding the Solution Since $\frac{11}{15}$ is already in simplest form, no further steps are necessary for solving the problem. You can use estimation to check that the sum is reasonable. Round each fraction to 0, $\frac{1}{2}$, or 1, and then add. In this problem, $\frac{1}{3}$ is about $\frac{1}{2}$ and $\frac{2}{5}$ is about $\frac{1}{2}$, so $\frac{1}{2} + \frac{1}{2} = 1$. $\frac{11}{15}$ is close to 1, so the answer is reasonable.

TRY IT!

A soup recipe calls for $\frac{1}{4}$ cup of chicken broth and $\frac{2}{3}$ cup of water. How much chicken broth and water does the recipe use?

EXAMPLE 2

Jacob needs $\frac{2}{3}$ yard of purple fabric and $\frac{3}{8}$ yard of yellow fabric to make a flag. How much more purple fabric does he need than yellow fabric?

You can solve this problem by renaming the fractions with a common denominator and subtracting.

The LCD of $\frac{2}{3}$ and $\frac{3}{8}$ is 24. Rename the fractions using the LCD.

$$\frac{2}{3} \rightarrow \frac{2 \times 8}{3 \times 8} = \frac{16}{24} \text{ and } \frac{3}{8} \rightarrow \frac{3 \times 3}{8 \times 3} = \frac{9}{24}$$

Subtract the like fractions by subtracting the numerators. The denominator stays the same.

$$\frac{16}{24} - \frac{9}{24} = \frac{16 - 9}{24}$$
$$= \frac{7}{24}$$

So, Jacob needs $\frac{7}{24}$ yard more purple fabric than yellow fabric.

▶ **Understanding the Solution**   The problem requires subtraction since the original problem asks *how much more* purple fabric than yellow is needed. You can check for reasonableness by estimating. $\frac{2}{3}$ is about 1, $\frac{3}{8}$ is about $\frac{1}{2}$, and $1 - \frac{1}{2}$ is $\frac{1}{2}$. $\frac{7}{24}$ is close to $\frac{1}{2}$, so the answer is reasonable.

TRY IT!

Brady and Katrina ate $\frac{5}{6}$ of a cheese pizza and $\frac{1}{2}$ of a spinach and mushroom pizza. How much more of the cheese pizza did they eat than the spinach and mushroom pizza?

Exercises

SHORT RESPONSE

1 At the Uptown Pet Shop, $\frac{3}{5}$ of the birds are parakeets and $\frac{1}{4}$ are parrots. What fraction of the birds at the pet shop are parakeets or parrots? Write your answer in simplest form.

Show your work.

Answer _____

2 At a birthday party, $\frac{3}{8}$ of the presents were wrapped and $\frac{1}{3}$ were in gift bags. What fraction of the presents were wrapped or in gift bags?

A $\frac{1}{24}$

B $\frac{2}{11}$

C $\frac{4}{11}$

D $\frac{17}{24}$

3 Damian rode his bicycle $\frac{5}{6}$ mile Saturday morning and $\frac{3}{4}$ mile Saturday afternoon. How much farther did he ride his bicycle in the morning than the afternoon?

A $\frac{4}{5}$ mile

B $\frac{5}{12}$ mile

C $\frac{1}{5}$ mile

D $\frac{1}{12}$ mile

4 Chloe bought $\frac{7}{8}$ yard of trim to make a decorative border around a photo frame. She used $\frac{3}{4}$ yard. What fraction of a yard is left?

A $\frac{5}{16}$

B $\frac{1}{8}$

C $\frac{1}{3}$

D $\frac{5}{6}$

5 In a vote of favorite sports teams, $\frac{4}{9}$ of the class voted for the Yankees and $\frac{1}{6}$ voted for the Mets. What fraction of the class voted for the Yankees or Mets?

A $\frac{5}{18}$

B $\frac{1}{3}$

C $\frac{11}{18}$

D $\frac{4}{5}$

6 Anthony and Marilia are sending invitations for a fund raiser. Anthony sent $\frac{3}{5}$ of the invitations on the list and Marilia sent $\frac{1}{3}$ on the list. What fraction of the invitations did Anthony and Marilia send?

A $\frac{14}{15}$

B $\frac{3}{8}$

C $\frac{4}{15}$

D $\frac{1}{4}$

7 In a survey of students at the school library, $\frac{7}{20}$ said they preferred reading science fiction novels and $\frac{1}{4}$ said they preferred reading mystery stories. How much greater is the fraction of students who preferred science fiction novels to mystery stories?

A $\frac{1}{10}$

B $\frac{3}{10}$

C $\frac{3}{5}$

D $\frac{1}{3}$

8 Brad, Pala, and Rami want to make tails for their kites. The lengths of material they need for their kites are shown below:

Brad: $\frac{1}{6}$ yard of material

Pala: $\frac{1}{2}$ yard of material

Rami: $\frac{2}{9}$ yard of material

Part A

If Brad, Pala, and Rami work together to make their kite tails, how much material will they need altogether? Write your answer in simplest form.

Show your work.

Answer _____

Part B

Suppose Brad and Pala work together and Rami works alone. How much more material will Brad and Pala need than Rami? Write your answer in simplest form.

Show your work.

Answer _____

LESSON 5.3   Multiplying and Dividing Fractions

New York Performance Indicators

6.N.17 Multiply and divide fractions with unlike denominators

6.N.19 Identify the multiplicative inverse (reciprocal) of a number

6.PS.13 Model problems with pictures/diagrams or physical objects

6.CN.7 Apply mathematics to problem situations that develop outside of mathematics

VOCABULARY

The **multiplicative inverse** of a number is the number that, when multiplied by a given number, results in a product of one.

The **reciprocal** of a number is the multiplicative inverse of the number.

REVIEW

Understanding Multiplying and Dividing Fractions

- To multiply fractions, multiply the numerators and then the denominators.

$$\frac{1}{4} \times \frac{5}{6} = \frac{5}{24}$$

- To divide by a fraction, multiply by the multiplicative inverse.

$$\frac{1}{4} \div \frac{5}{6} = \frac{1}{4} \times \frac{6}{5} = \frac{6}{20} \text{ or } \frac{3}{10}$$

What You Should Know

The word *of* indicates multiplication. For example, if $\frac{1}{2}$ of the students in your class chew gum, and $\frac{3}{5}$ of those students chew sugarless gum, then multiply $\frac{3}{5} \times \frac{1}{2}$ to find the fraction of students in your class who chew sugarless gum.

$$\frac{3}{5} \times \frac{1}{2} = \frac{3}{10}$$

Multiplying Fractions

To multiply by a fraction, multiply the numerators and then the denominators. You can simplify before you multiply if the numerator of one fraction and the denominator of another fraction have a common factor. Write products in simplest form.

EXAMPLE 1

Tracy and Devin are walking $\frac{5}{6}$ mile in a walkathon to raise money for the Red Cross. They walked $\frac{3}{4}$ of the distance in thirty minutes. How far did they walk in thirty minutes?

You can solve this problem by multiplying the fractions.

Multiply $\frac{3}{4} \times \frac{5}{6}$.

Notice that the numerator of one fraction and the denominator of another fraction have a common factor of 3. So you can simplify before multiplying the numerators and denominators.

$$\frac{3}{4} \times \frac{5}{6} = \frac{\overset{1}{\cancel{3}} \times 5}{4 \times \underset{2}{\cancel{6}}} = \frac{5}{8}$$

Tracy and Devin walked $\frac{5}{8}$ mile in thirty minutes.

▶ **Understanding the Solution**   The product of the fractions should be less than either fraction because multiplying a fraction by a fraction is taking part of a part. In this example, the product, $\frac{5}{8}$, is less than either factor. $\frac{5}{8} < \frac{3}{4}$ and $\frac{5}{8} < \frac{5}{6}$

TRY IT!

Teri wants to make $\frac{1}{2}$ of a recipe that calls for $\frac{3}{4}$ cup of yogurt. How many cups of yogurt should she use?

Dividing Fractions

To divide by a fraction, multiply by the multiplicative inverse of the divisor. Then use the same process for dividing fractions that you use for multiplying fractions. Note: The multiplicative inverse of a number if often referred to as the reciprocal of the number.

EXAMPLE 2

An electrician has a $\frac{5}{6}$-foot piece of wire that he wants to cut into $\frac{1}{3}$-foot lengths. How many $\frac{1}{3}$-foot pieces will he have after he cuts the wire?

You can solve this problem by dividing $\frac{5}{6} \div \frac{1}{3}$.

Identify the multiplicative inverse of $\frac{1}{3}$ and then multiply the numerators and multiply the denominators of the fractions.

The multiplicative inverse of $\frac{1}{3}$ is $\frac{3}{1}$ because $\frac{1}{3} \times \frac{3}{1} = \frac{3}{3}$ or 1.

$$\frac{5}{6} \div \frac{1}{3} = \frac{5}{6} \times \frac{3}{1} = \frac{5 \times \overset{1}{\cancel{3}}}{\underset{2}{\cancel{6}} \times 1} = \frac{5}{2}$$

Simplify the product by writing it as a mixed number. $\frac{5}{2} = 2\frac{1}{2}$

The electrician will have $2\frac{1}{2}$ pieces of $\frac{1}{3}$-foot long wires.

▶ **Understanding the Solution**   The solution means that there are $2\frac{1}{2}$ one-thirds in $\frac{5}{6}$. So, the electrician has 2 pieces of wire that are $\frac{1}{3}$-foot long and 1 piece that is $\frac{1}{2}$ of $\frac{1}{3}$ foot long or $\frac{1}{6}$ foot. If you add $\frac{1}{3} + \frac{1}{3} + \frac{1}{6}$, the sum is $\frac{5}{6}$. $\left(\frac{1}{3} + \frac{1}{3} + \frac{1}{6} = \frac{2}{6} + \frac{2}{6} + \frac{1}{6} = \frac{5}{6}\right)$ When dividing by a fraction that is less than 1, the quotient is always greater than the dividend. In this example, $2\frac{1}{2} > \frac{5}{6}$.

TRY IT!

A caterer has 8 pounds of ham for making party trays. If she uses $\frac{2}{3}$-pound of ham for each tray, how many party trays can she make?

Exercises

SHORT RESPONSE

1 During gym class, $\frac{3}{8}$ of the students chose basketball as the sport they wanted to play, and $\frac{2}{5}$ of those students chose guard as the position they want to play. What fraction of the gym class wants to play both basketball and the position of guard?

Show your work.

Answer _____

2 Which expression is equivalent to $\frac{4}{5} \div \frac{3}{8}$?

 A $\frac{4}{5} \times \frac{3}{8}$

 B $\frac{4}{5} \times \frac{8}{3}$

 C $\frac{5}{4} \times \frac{3}{8}$

 D $\frac{5}{4} \div \frac{3}{8}$

3 Kyle made 24 cups of clam chowder. If a serving is $\frac{3}{4}$ cup, how many servings did he make?

 A 9

 B 14

 C 18

 D 32

4 After a visit to the zoo, $\frac{5}{8}$ of the students voted primates as their favorite animal, and $\frac{2}{5}$ of those students liked the gorillas best. What fraction of the students voted for gorillas?

 A $\frac{16}{25}$

 B $\frac{3}{8}$

 C $\frac{1}{4}$

 D $\frac{9}{40}$

5 Tyler cut a $\frac{2}{3}$-foot sandwich into $\frac{1}{6}$-foot pieces. How many pieces did he cut?

 A 2

 B 3

 C 4

 D 6

6 What value for n makes the equation true?

$6 \times n = 1$

 A -6

 B $\frac{1}{6}$

 C $\frac{5}{6}$

 D 1

7 Mai used $\frac{4}{9}$ of $\frac{3}{4}$ yard of felt for a bulletin board display. How much felt did she use?

 A $\frac{1}{5}$ yd

 B $\frac{1}{3}$ yd

 C $\frac{16}{27}$ yd

 D $\frac{12}{13}$ yd

8 A landscape architect is designing a 12-acre park. He wants to plant sections that are $\frac{2}{5}$ acres each.

Part A

Explain how you can find the number of $\frac{2}{5}$-acre sections there will be in the park. Then find the number of sections.

Show your work.

Answer _____

Part B

So far, the landscape architect knows he wants to plant $\frac{3}{4}$ of one of the $\frac{2}{5}$-acre sections in dogwoods.

What fraction of an acre will be planted in dogwoods?

Show your work.

Answer _____

Adding and Subtracting Mixed Numbers with Unlike Denominators

New York Performance Indicators

6.N.18 Add, subtract, multiply, and divide mixed numbers with unlike denominators
6.PS.23 Verify results of a problem
6.CN.7 Apply mathematics to problem situations that develop outside of mathematics

VOCABULARY

A **mixed number** is the sum of a whole number and a fraction. Example: $3\frac{1}{3}$

REVIEW

Understanding Adding and Subtracting Mixed Numbers with Unlike Denominators

When adding or subtracting mixed numbers with unlike denominators,

- Rename the fractions so they have like denominators
- Add or subtract the fractions
- Add or subtract the whole numbers

To subtract $12\frac{3}{4} - 6\frac{1}{3}$, you would first rename the fractions with the LCD of 12 to give $12\frac{9}{12} - 6\frac{4}{12}$. You would subtract the like fractions first ($\frac{9}{12} - \frac{4}{12} = \frac{5}{12}$). Then subtract the whole numbers ($12 - 6 = 6$). So $12\frac{3}{4} - 6\frac{1}{3} = 6\frac{5}{12}$.

Applying Adding and Subtracting Mixed Numbers with Unlike Denominators

Joaquin is shipping two packages to his uncle in Buffalo. One package weighs $4\frac{5}{8}$ pounds, and the other weighs $3\frac{1}{4}$ pounds. What is the combined weight of the two packages?

Add $4\frac{5}{8} + 3\frac{1}{4}$. Rename $\frac{1}{4}$. Add the fractions and then the whole numbers.

$$4\frac{5}{8} + 3\frac{1}{4} \rightarrow 4\frac{5}{8} + 3\frac{2}{8} = 7\frac{7}{8}$$

The two packages weigh $7\frac{7}{8}$ pounds.

Renaming Fractions to Add and Subtract Mixed Numbers

When adding or subtracting mixed numbers with unlike fractions, you must rename the fractions of mixed numbers. Next, add or subtract the fractions. Then add or subtract the whole numbers and simplify if necessary.

EXAMPLE 1

Lily and Rikki went horseback riding in the Adirondacks. They rode $4\frac{7}{10}$ miles to a trail junction and then rode another trail for $1\frac{4}{5}$ miles. How far did they ride?

You can solve this problem by adding $4\frac{7}{10}$ and $1\frac{4}{5}$.

Write the problem.		Rename the fractions.		Add and simplify.
$4\frac{7}{10}$	$\longrightarrow$	$\frac{7}{10}$	$\longrightarrow$	$4\frac{7}{10}$
$+1\frac{4}{5}$	$\longrightarrow$	$\frac{4 \times 2}{5 \times 2}$	$\longrightarrow$	$+1\frac{8}{10}$

$$5\frac{15}{10} \longrightarrow 5 + 1\frac{5}{10} \longrightarrow 6\frac{5}{10} \text{ or } 6\frac{1}{2}$$

So Lily and Rikki rode $6\frac{1}{2}$ miles.

▶ **Understanding the Solution** You can estimate to check for reasonableness. Round each mixed number in the original problem to the nearest whole number and add. $4\frac{7}{10}$ rounds to 5 and $1\frac{4}{5}$ rounds to 2: $5 + 2 = 7$. 7 is close to $6\frac{1}{2}$, so the answer is reasonable.

TRY IT!

It took Emily $2\frac{1}{4}$ hours to write a report for science and $1\frac{1}{3}$ hours to finish her math homework. How many hours did she spend on science and math homework?

EXAMPLE 2

Manuel cut a length of balsa wood from a strip that is $15\frac{1}{2}$ inches long. The strip is now $7\frac{3}{8}$ inches long. What is the length of balsa wood that Manuel cut?

You can solve this problem by subtracting $15\frac{1}{2} - 7\frac{3}{8}$.

Write the problem.		Rename the fractions.		Subtract and simplify, if necessaary.
$15\frac{1}{2}$	$\longrightarrow$	$\frac{1 \times 4}{2 \times 4}$	$\longrightarrow$	$15\frac{4}{8}$
$-7\frac{3}{8}$	$\longrightarrow$	$\frac{3}{8}$	$\longrightarrow$	$-7\frac{3}{8}$
				$8\frac{1}{8}$

So, the length of balsa wood is $8\frac{1}{8}$ inches.

▶ **Understanding the Solution** You can verify the solution by adding $8\frac{1}{8} + 7\frac{3}{8}$. Since the sum is $15\frac{4}{8}$ or $15\frac{1}{2}$ in simplest form, the solution checks.

TRY IT!

The length of a table is $7\frac{2}{3}$ feet. The width is $3\frac{1}{6}$ feet. How much longer is the length of the table than the width?

Renaming Mixed Numbers to Subtract

Sometimes it is necessary to rename a whole number when subtracting mixed numbers. If the fraction in the second number (subtrahend) is larger than the fraction in the first number (minuend), you must rename the mixed number as a whole number and improper fraction.

EXAMPLE 3

Ned chopped $4\frac{1}{3}$ cups of mushrooms for two batches of stir fry. If he uses $2\frac{3}{4}$ cups for the first stir fry, how many cups will he have for the second?

You can solve this problem by subtracting $4\frac{1}{3} - 2\frac{3}{4}$.

Write the problem.

$$4\frac{1}{3}$$
$$-2\frac{3}{4}$$

$\longrightarrow$

Rename the fractions using their LCD.

$$4\frac{4}{12}$$
$$-2\frac{9}{12}$$

$\longrightarrow$

Rename $4\frac{4}{12}$ as $3\frac{12}{12} + \frac{4}{12}$. Subtract.

$$3\frac{16}{12}$$
$$-2\frac{9}{12}$$
$$1\frac{7}{12}$$

Ned has $1\frac{7}{12}$ cups of mushrooms for the second stir fry.

▶ **Understanding the Solution**   The key to solving problems in which you rename the mixed number is remembering to add the fraction part of the original mixed number to the renamed mixed number. To avoid this error, write an expression to show the renaming. For example, rename $6\frac{3}{8}$ as $5\frac{8}{8} + \frac{3}{8}$ or $5\frac{11}{8}$.

TRY IT!

Jenna lives $8\frac{2}{5}$ miles from the train station and $3\frac{5}{6}$ miles from the subway. How much closer does she live to the subway than the train station?

Exercises

SHORT RESPONSE

1 Tara bought $5\frac{1}{4}$ yards of material to make a costume for a school party. She used $3\frac{2}{3}$ yards for the costume. How much material is left? Write your answer in simplest form.
Show your work.

Answer _____

2 An Eastern Meadowlark weighs between $3\frac{9}{50}$ ounces and $5\frac{3}{10}$ ounces. What is the range of weight for the songbird?

A $2\frac{3}{25}$

B $2\frac{1}{10}$

C $8\frac{1}{5}$

D $8\frac{12}{25}$

3 The snowfall on Monday was $2\frac{5}{8}$ inches. On Tuesday, it was $1\frac{11}{16}$ inches. What was the total snowfall?

A $\frac{15}{16}$ inches

B $1\frac{1}{4}$ inches

C $3\frac{2}{3}$ inches

D $4\frac{5}{16}$ inches

4 Austin bought $4\frac{2}{3}$ pounds of pecans and $2\frac{7}{8}$ pounds of walnuts to make a nut mixture. How many more pounds of pecans did he buy?

A $7\frac{13}{24}$

B $6\frac{9}{11}$

C $2\frac{5}{11}$

D $1\frac{19}{24}$

5 A carpenter needs $3\frac{1}{3}$ quarts of stain for a table and $2\frac{3}{4}$ quarts for a plant stand. How many quarts of stain does the carpenter need?

A $6\frac{1}{12}$

B $5\frac{3}{7}$

C $1\frac{2}{7}$

D $\frac{7}{12}$

6 Kelli rode $4\frac{4}{5}$ miles of trail on his mountain bike on Thursday, $5\frac{3}{4}$ miles on Friday, and $3\frac{9}{10}$ miles on Saturday. How many total miles did she bike?

A $16\frac{7}{20}$

B $14\frac{2}{5}$

C $14\frac{9}{20}$

D $12\frac{1}{2}$

7 Nadia cut a $4\frac{1}{2}$-foot piece of rope from a rope that was $9\frac{2}{3}$ feet long. How long is the rope now?

A $4\frac{1}{6}$ feet

B $5\frac{1}{6}$ feet

C $5\frac{1}{5}$ feet

D $14\frac{1}{6}$ feet

8 Derek plans to burn a CD with some of his favorite music. Some of the song lengths are shown in the table below.

Song	Length (minutes)
1	$7\frac{11}{12}$
2	$12\frac{2}{3}$
3	$4\frac{5}{6}$
4	$9\frac{5}{12}$

PART A

What is the total length in minutes for the four songs? Write your answer in simplest form.

Show your work.

Expression _____

PART B

Derek has already recorded $42\frac{3}{4}$ minutes. Does he have enough room to record all of the songs in his list if the CD can record $80\frac{1}{2}$ minutes? Explain.

Show your work.

Answer _____

_____

LESSON 5.5 Multiplying and Dividing Mixed Numbers

New York Performance Indicators

6.N.18 Add, subtract, multiply, and divide mixed numbers with unlike denominators
6.PS.23 Verify results of a problem
6.CN.3 Connect and apply mathematical information to solve problems
6.CN.7 Apply mathematics to problem situations that develop outside of mathematics

VOCABULARY

An **improper fraction** is a fraction that has a numerator that is greater than or equal to the denominator.

REVIEW

Understanding Multiplying and Dividing Mixed Numbers

To multiply mixed numbers with unlike denominators, write the mixed numbers as improper fractions. Then multiply the numerators and multiply the denominators.

Simplify before you multiply, if possible.

$$2\frac{2}{5} \times 4\frac{1}{2} = \frac{12}{5} \times \frac{9}{2}$$

$$= \frac{\overset{6}{\cancel{12}} \times 9}{5 \times \cancel{2}}$$
$$= \frac{54}{5} \text{ or } 10\frac{4}{5}$$

To divide mixed numbers with unlike denominators, write the mixed numbers as improper fractions and then multiply by the multiplicative inverse of the divisor.

$$5\frac{1}{4} \div 1\frac{2}{3} = \frac{21}{4} \times \frac{3}{5}$$

$$= \frac{63}{20} \text{ or } 3\frac{3}{20}$$

Applying Multiplying and Dividing Mixed Numbers

Ava has $3\frac{3}{4}$ cups of flour to make a gingerbread cake for a school party. If she needs $1\frac{1}{2}$ cups of flour for each cake, how many gingerbread cakes can she make?

Divide $3\frac{3}{4} \div 1\frac{1}{2}$ to solve the problem. Write the mixed numbers as improper fractions and then multiply by the multiplicative inverse of $\frac{3}{2}$, which is $\frac{2}{3}$.

$$3\frac{3}{4} \div 1\frac{1}{2} = \frac{15}{4} \div \frac{3}{2}$$

$$= \frac{15}{4} \times \frac{2}{3}$$
$$= \frac{\overset{5}{\cancel{15}} \times \overset{1}{\cancel{2}}}{\underset{2}{\cancel{4}} \times \underset{1}{\cancel{3}}}$$
$$= \frac{5}{2} \text{ or } 2\frac{1}{2}.$$

Ava can make 2 gingerbread cakes.

Multiplying and Dividing Mixed Numbers with Unlike Denominators

Write mixed numbers as improper fractions before you multiply or divide. Then multiply and divide the same way that you multiply and divide fractions. Remember to multiply by the multiplicative inverse or reciprocal when you divide mixed numbers.

EXAMPLE 1

Dena can run one lap around the track in $1\frac{3}{5}$ minutes. How long would it take her to run $6\frac{1}{2}$ laps?

You can solve this problem by multiplying the mixed numbers.

$1\frac{3}{5} \times 6\frac{1}{2} = \frac{8}{5} \times \frac{13}{2}$ Rewrite the mixed numbers as improper fractions.

$= \frac{\overset{4}{\cancel{8}} \times 13}{5 \times \cancel{2}}$ Multiply the numerators and multiply the denominators.
$\phantom{= \frac{8 \times 13}{5 \times 2}}_{1}$

$= \frac{52}{5}$ or $10\frac{2}{5}$ Simplify.

So Dena can run $6\frac{1}{2}$ laps in $10\frac{2}{5}$ minutes.

▶ **Understanding the Solution** You can estimate to check the answer for reasonableness. Since the fraction parts of both mixed numbers are close to $\frac{1}{2}$, round $1\frac{3}{5}$ up to 2 and $6\frac{1}{2}$ down to 6 and multiply. $2 \times 6 = 12$ and 12 is close to $10\frac{2}{5}$, so the answer is reasonable.

TRY IT!

A garden is $2\frac{4}{9}$ yards long and $2\frac{1}{4}$ yards wide. What is the area of the garden?

EXAMPLE 2

Tyson typed a $20\frac{1}{2}$ -page report on early Iroquois history in $2\frac{2}{3}$ hours. On average, how many pages did Tyson type per hour?

You can solve this problem by dividing $20\frac{1}{2} \div 2\frac{2}{3}$.

$20\frac{1}{2} \div 2\frac{2}{3} = \frac{41}{2} \div \frac{8}{3}$ Write the numbers as improper fractions.

$= \frac{41}{2} \times \frac{3}{8}$ Multiply using the multiplicative inverse of $\frac{8}{3}$.

$= \frac{123}{16}$ or $7\frac{11}{16}$ Multiply the numerators and denominator. Simplify.

Tyson typed an average of $7\frac{11}{16}$ pages per hour.

▶ **Understanding the Solution** Check the answer for reasonableness by using compatible numbers to estimate. The compatible numbers close to $20\frac{1}{2}$ and $2\frac{2}{3}$ are 21 and 3. Since $21 \div 3 = 7$ and 7 is close to $7\frac{1}{2}$, the answer is reasonable.

TRY IT!

Brandon drove $98\frac{1}{2}$ miles in $1\frac{3}{4}$ hours. What was his average speed?

EXAMPLE 3

Sophia is using $2\frac{1}{4}$-inch tiles to tile the $40\frac{1}{2}$-inch backsplash in her kitchen. How many tiles does she need?

You can solve this problem by dividing $40\frac{1}{2} \div 2\frac{1}{4}$.

$40\frac{1}{2} \div 2\frac{1}{4} = \frac{81}{2} \div \frac{9}{4}$ Write the numbers as improper fractions.

$= \frac{81}{2} \times \frac{4}{9}$ Multiply using the multiplicative inverse of $\frac{8}{3}$.

$= \frac{\overset{9}{\cancel{81}} \times \overset{2}{\cancel{4}}}{\underset{1}{\cancel{2}} \times \underset{1}{\cancel{9}}}$ Multiply the numerators and denominator.

$= \frac{18}{1} = 18$ Simplify.

Sophia needs 18 tiles.

▶ **Understanding the Solution** You can verify the results by multiplying the quotient and the divisor. The product should equal the dividend.

$18 \times 2\frac{1}{4} = \frac{18}{1} \times \frac{9}{4} = \frac{\overset{9}{\cancel{18}} \times 9}{1 \times \underset{2}{\cancel{4}}} = \frac{81}{2} = 40\frac{1}{2}$. The solution checks.

TRY IT!

The area of a rectangle is $20\frac{5}{8}$ ft². What is the width if the length is $3\frac{3}{4}$ ft?

Exercises

SHORT RESPONSE

1 Jill's dog Fiona weighs $8\frac{1}{4}$ pounds. Her dog Felix weighs $1\frac{1}{2}$ times as much as Fiona. How much does Felix weigh?

Show your work.

Answer _____

2 A recipe calls for $1\frac{2}{3}$ cups of oats for each batch of trail bars. How many cups of oats do you need if you make $2\frac{1}{2}$ batches?

A $\frac{2}{3}$

B $3\frac{3}{5}$

C $4\frac{1}{6}$

D $4\frac{2}{3}$

3 A cherry tree grew $5\frac{3}{4}$ feet in $3\frac{1}{2}$ months. What was the average growth per month?

A $1\frac{9}{14}$ inches

B $2\frac{1}{4}$ inches

C $9\frac{1}{4}$ inches

D $20\frac{1}{8}$ inches

4 The track at Cassie's school is $2\frac{3}{5}$ miles. Cassie ran around the track $2\frac{3}{4}$ times. How many miles did she run?

A $5\frac{7}{20}$

B $7\frac{3}{20}$

C $4\frac{2}{3}$

D $9\frac{9}{10}$

5 Carli wants to put some prints that are $4\frac{1}{2}$ inches wide side-by-side on a wall that is $26\frac{1}{4}$ inches wide. How many prints can she place on the wall?

A 6

B 5

C 4

D 3

6 A shuttle bus at an amusement park completes its route in $1\frac{2}{3}$ hours. How many routes can be completed in $6\frac{1}{2}$ hours?

A 3

B 4

C 8

D 10

7 Mr. Billings wants to increase the size of the dining room by increasing the width $1\frac{1}{4}$ times. What will be the new width of the dining room if the old width is $4\frac{2}{3}$ feet?

A $3\frac{5}{12}$ ft

B $5\frac{3}{7}$ ft

C $5\frac{5}{6}$ ft

D $5\frac{11}{12}$ ft

8 An object that weighs one pound on Earth can weigh much more than that on other planets. The list below shows how much more an object can weigh on other planets.

Jupiter: $2\frac{1}{2}$ times Earth weight

Neptune: $1\frac{1}{5}$ times Earth weight

Part A

What would be the weight of a $12\frac{3}{4}$-pound bowling ball on Jupiter and Neptune?
Show your work.

Answer _____

Part B

Suppose a backpack weighs $44\frac{1}{2}$ pounds on Jupiter. How much does it weigh on Earth?
Show your work.

Answer _____

Relating Fractions, Decimals, and Percents

New York Performance Indicators

6.N.20 Represent fractions as terminating or repeating decimals

6.N.21 Find multiple representations of rational numbers (fractions, decimals, and percents 0 to 100)

6.PS.11 Translate from a picture/diagram to a number or symbolic expression

6.CN.2 Explore and explain the relationship between mathematical ideas

6.CN.4 Understand multiple representations and how they are related

VOCABULARY

A **repeating decimal** is a decimal in which a pattern of one or more digits is repeated indefinitely.

A **terminating** decimal is a decimal that ends.

REVIEW

Understanding Fractions, Decimals, and Percents

The 10 × 10 grid below can be used to represent a fraction, decimal, and percent.

45 squares are shaded.

Fraction: $\frac{45}{100}$ or $\frac{9}{20}$

Decimal: 0.45, read as 45 hundredths

Percent: 45 out of 100 or 45%

Applying Fractions, Decimals, and Percents

In a survey of sixth grade students at Brookdale Middle School, 14 out of 100 students knew that the ladybug is New York's state insect.

Write the results of the survey as a fraction, decimal, and percent. Write the fraction in simplest form.

Fraction

14 out of 100 = $\frac{14}{100} = \frac{7}{50}$

Decimal

$\frac{14}{100} = 0.14$, read as 14 hundredths

Percent

14 out of 100 = 14%

Writing Percents as Fractions and Decimals

- Write percents as fractions by writing the percent as the numerator over a denominator of 100 and then simplifying, if necessary.

- Write a percent as a decimal by first writing it as a fraction with a denominator of 100, and then as a decimal.

EXAMPLE 1

Caitlin is practicing for a spelling bee contest. In her first trial run, she spelled 88% of the words correctly. Write 88% as a fraction and a decimal.

You can solve this problem by writing the percent as a fraction with a denominator of 100. 88% means 88 out of 100, so write 88 over a denominator of 100. Use the GCF of the numerator and denominator to simplify the fraction.

$$88\% = \frac{88}{100} = \frac{\overset{22}{\cancel{88}}}{\underset{25}{\cancel{100}}} \text{ or } \frac{22}{25}$$

To write 88% as a decimal, first write the percent as a fraction with a denominator of 100 and then as a decimal.

$$88\% = \frac{88}{100} = 0.88, \text{ read as 88 hundredths}$$

So 88% is $\frac{22}{25}$ written as a fraction, and 0.88 written as a decimal.

▶ **Understanding the Solution**   You can also write a percent as a decimal by moving the decimal point two places to the left, which is the same as dividing by a hundred.

$$88\% = 88\% = 0.88$$

TRY IT!

The school sign-up sheet for volleyball has 48% sixth graders. What fraction and decimal are equivalent to 48%?

Writing Fractions as Decimals and Percents

You can write fractions as decimals by dividing the numerator of the fraction by the denominator or by writing equivalent fractions with denominators of 10, 100, or 1,000.

EXAMPLE 2

At the wildlife center, $\frac{6}{25}$ of the birds are herons. What is $\frac{6}{25}$ written as a decimal and as a percent?

You can solve this problem by writing the fraction with a denominator of 100.
The denominator of $\frac{6}{25}$ is a factor of 100, so you can write the equivalent fraction with a denominator of 100 and then write it as a decimal. Multiply the numerator and denominator by 4 since $4 \times 25 = 100$.

$$\frac{6}{25} = \frac{6 \times 4}{25 \times 4}$$
$$= \frac{24}{100}$$
$$= 0.24 \text{ or } 24\%$$

► **Understanding the Solution**   Dividing 24 by 100 gives you 0.24. Since the equivalent fraction has a denominator of 10.0, you know that $\frac{6}{25}$ = 24%.

You could also write $\frac{6}{25}$ as a decimal by dividing 6 by 25. The result, 0.24, is a terminating decimal. You must use this division method for any fraction whose denominator is not a factor of 10, 100, or 1,000, such as $\frac{3}{8}$ or $\frac{4}{9}$.

3 ÷ 8 results in the terminating decimal 0.375

4 ÷ 9 results in the repeating decimal 0.4444. . .

TRY IT!

In a sand sculpture contest, $\frac{10}{11}$ sculptures are castles. What is $\frac{10}{11}$ written as a decimal?

Writing Decimals as Fractions and Percents

Write decimals as fractions by using place value to write the decimal as tenths, hundredths, or thousandths. Write decimals as percents by writing the decimal as a fraction with a denominator of 100. Then write the fraction as a percent.

EXAMPLE 3

A garden snail has an average speed of 0.03 mph. What is the speed written as a fraction and a percent?

You can solve this problem by writing the decimal as a fraction and then as a percent. The place value of 0.03 is hundredths, so write 3 over a denominator of 100 to write the decimal as a fraction. Then write the fraction as a percent.

$0.03 = \frac{3}{100} = 3\%$

So, 0.03 is $\frac{3}{100}$ written as a fraction and 3% written as a percent.

► **Understanding the Solution**   Place value is important when writing a decimal as a fraction. Always identify the place value of the last decimal place before writing the fraction. Also simplify as needed.

TRY IT!

A three-toed sloth has an average speed of 0.15 mph. What is 0.15 written as a fraction and a decimal?

Exercises

1 In the astronomy club, 72% of the students voted for science as their favorite subject in school. What is 72% written as a fraction and a decimal?

Show your work.

Answer _____

MULTIPLE CHOICE

2 Trina bought a carton of milk that had 2% milk fat. Which fraction is equivalent to 2%?

A $\frac{1}{50}$

B $\frac{1}{20}$

C $\frac{1}{5}$

D $\frac{1}{2}$

3 At the school carnival, Nick tossed $\frac{5}{11}$ of the bean bags into the 1,000-point hole. Which decimal is equivalent to $\frac{5}{11}$?

A 0.11

B 0.454545…

C 0.5

D 0.511

4 Emma scored $\frac{4}{5}$ of the goals in the last soccer game. What percent of the goals did she score?

A 8%

B 45%

C 54%

D 80%

5 In 2001, industry consumed 16% of New York's energy resources. What is 16% written as a decimal?

A 0.16

B 0.4

C 0.425

D 1.6

6 An essential oil blend is 0.05 lavender. What percent of the blend is lavender?

A 50%

B 5%

C 0.5%

D 0.05%

7 The length of a ladybug can be as short as 0.16 inch. What is the fraction equivalent of 0.16?

A $\frac{3}{50}$ inch

B $\frac{1}{6}$ inch

C $\frac{4}{25}$ inch

D $\frac{6}{10}$ inch

8 A toy store put together a giant grab bag of toys to give away for the grand opening. The table below shows a breakdown of the toys in the grab bag, given either as fractions, decimals, or percents. The table has not been completed.

Grab Bag Toys			
Toy	**Fraction**	**Decimal**	**Percent**
Action Figure			18%
Board Game	$\frac{1}{50}$		
Building Blocks		0.32	
Mini-Basketball	$\frac{7}{20}$		
Puzzle			13%

Part A

Complete the table by filling in the missing fractions, decimals, and percents. Write fractions in simplest form.

Show your work.

Grab Bag Toys			
Toy	**Fraction**	**Decimal**	**Percent**
Action Figure			18%
Board Game	$\frac{1}{50}$		
Building Blocks		0.32	
Mini-Basketball	$\frac{7}{20}$		
Puzzle			13%

Part B

Suppose the store gave away only 90% of the toys in the grab bag. What percent of the toys did the store not give away? What are the fraction and decimal equivalents of the toys not given away?

Show your work.

Answer _____

LESSON 5.7 Problem-Solving Strategy: Making an Organized List

New York Performance Indicators

6.PS.15 Make organized lists or charts to solve numerical problems

Understand the Strategy

Making an organized list is a strategy that can be used to solve a problem when all possible ways or combinations need to be found. It is often helpful to organize information in numerical order.

Problem: You have four cards, each with a different number on it. The cards are numbered with a 2, 3, 4, or 8. How many different sums are possible using two cards at a time?

SOLUTION

What do you know?

There are 4 cards.

The cards are numbered 2, 3, 4, 8.

What do you need to find?

How many different sums are possible using 2 cards?

Find the relationship.

How would you find the different sums? Try pairing the card with a 2 on it with each of the other cards and finding each sum. Then pair the card with 3 on it with the cards it has not been paired with and find their sums. Continue with the remaining cards.

$$2 + 3 = 5 \qquad 3 + 4 = 7 \qquad 4 + 8 = 12$$
$$2 + 4 = 6 \qquad 3 + 8 = 11$$
$$2 + 8 = 10$$

There are 6 different sums possible when using two cards at a time.

Understanding the Solution The card with a 2 on it can be paired with three cards. The card with the 3 should only be paired with the cards with 4 and 8 on them. Pairing the card with 3 with the card with 2 would give the sum of 5, which you already have. The card with a 4 can only be paired with the card with an 8. The card with 4 on it has already been paired with the other cards. Pairing it again would not give a different sum. So there are only 6 different sums possible.

1 How many different ways can Kate write the product of 100 using two factors? Hint: The order in which the factors are written doesn't matter.

Show your work.

Answer _____

2 Jimmy pays for a package of pencils that cost 98¢ using the exact amount of money. He has quarters, dimes, and pennies. He does not have more than ten coins of any kind. How many different ways can he pay for the pencils?

Show your work.

Answer _____

LESSON 5.8   Understanding Exponents

New York Performance Indicators

6.N.23 Represent repeated multiplication in exponential form

6.N.24 Represent exponential form as repeated multiplication

6.N.25 Evaluate expressions having exponents where the power is an exponent of one, two, or three

6.PS.7 Represent problem situations verbally, numerically, algebraically, and/or graphically

6.PS.8 Select an appropriate representation of a problem

VOCABULARY

A **power** is a number that can be expressed using an exponent.

An **exponent** is the number in a power that shows how many times the base is used as a factor.

In a power, the **base** is the number used as a factor.

REVIEW

Understanding Exponents

If the same factor is used repeatedly in an expression, the factor can be written using an exponent and a base.

$$7 \times 7 \times 7 = 7^3 \leftarrow \text{exponent}$$
$$\uparrow$$
$$\text{base}$$

We say that 7^3 is a power. The base is 7 and the exponent is 3. Likewise, expressions that contain exponents can be written using repeated multiplication.

$$5^2 = 5 \times 5$$

If a number does not have an exponent, it is understood that the exponent is 1.

$$8 = 8^1$$

Applying Exponents

Kevin gave the answer to a question as 4×4. How could he have written his answer using an exponent?

$$4 \times 4 = 4^2$$

Writing Expressions as Repeated Multiplication and Powers

Numbers that are written as a product of the same factor can be written as a power using a base and exponent. Also, powers can be written as repeated multiplication.

EXAMPLE 1

John said his house number was 5^3. Write his house number using repeated multiplication.

You can solve this problem by writing the power using repeated multiplication.

The power 5^3 has a base of 5 and an exponent of 3. To write the number using repeated multiplication, write 5 as a factor three times.

$$5^3 = 5 \times 5 \times 5$$

▶ **Understanding the Solution** Since the exponent is 3 and the base is 5, 5 is used as a factor 3 times. $5^3 = 5 \times 5 \times 5$

TRY IT!

Write 11^2 using repeated multiplication.

EXAMPLE 2

Kim's savings account has 13 × 13 dollars in it. Write this amount of money using an exponent.

You can solve this problem by writing a power.

The expression 13×13 indicates that 13 is being used as a factor twice. This means the base is 13 and the exponent is 2.

$$13 \times 13 = 13^2$$

▶ **Understanding the Solution** The number 13 is used as a factor two times. So the exponent 2 is used to indicate this. The base of 13 is raised to the second power: 13^2.

TRY IT!

Write $4 \times 4 \times 4$ using an exponent.

Simplifying Expressions Involving Exponents

To simplify expressions with exponents, write each power as repeated multiplication with the same factor. Then multiply the factors together.

EXAMPLE 3

John said his brother's age is $2^3 \times 3^1$. How old is his brother?

You can solve this problem by simplifying the expression.

Write 2^3 and 3^1 using repeated multiplication. Then multiply the factors.

$$
\begin{aligned}
2^3 \times 3^1 &= 2 \times 2 \times 2 \times 3 & &\text{Write } 2^3 \text{ as a product. } 3^1 = 3. \\
&= 8 \times 3 & &\text{Multiply.} \\
&= 24 & &\text{Multiply.}
\end{aligned}
$$

▶ **Understanding the Solution** The power $2^3 = 2 \times 2 \times 2 = 8$ and the power $3^1 = 3$. The product of 8 and 3 is 24. So his brother is 24 years old.

TRY IT!

Simplify the expression $4^2 \times 5^2$.

Exercises

1 Mr. Jones earned $5^3 \times 3^3$ dollars one month. How much money did he earn?

Show your work.

Answer _____

2 A glass of skim milk contains $3^2 \times 10^1$ Calories. How many Calories are in a glass of skim milk?

Show your work.

Answer _____

MULTIPLE CHOICE

3 Which of the following shows $7^2 \times 6^3$ using repeated multiplication?

A $7 \times 2 \times 6 \times 3$
B $7 \times 7 \times 7 \times 6 \times 6$
C $7 \times 3 \times 6 \times 2$
D $7 \times 7 \times 6 \times 6 \times 6$

4 Simplify the expression $8^1 \times 9^3$.

A 216
B 4,608
C 5,184
D 5,832

5 Find the value of $3^3 \times 5^2$.

A 225
B 675
C 1,125
D 3,375

6 Richard's family traveled from their home to his grandparents' home, a distance of $2^3 \times 6^2$ miles. How many miles did his family travel?

A 96 miles
B 144 miles
C 288 miles
D 1,728 miles

7 The price of a new HDTV is about $5^2 \times 10^2$ dollars. About how much is the price of the new HDTV?

A $200
B $250
C $1,000
D $2,500

8 Write $6 \times 6 \times 7 \times 7 \times 2 \times 2 \times 2$ using exponents.

A $6^3 \times 7^2 \times 2^3$
B $6^2 \times 7^2 \times 2^3$
C $6^2 \times 7^1 \times 2^3$
D $6^2 \times 7^1 \times 2^2$

9 Your teacher writes the following on the board.

$7 \times 7 \times 2 \times 2 \times 4 \times 4 \times 4$

Part A

How would you write this expression using exponents?
Show your work.

Answer _____

Part B

One of your classmates gives the answer as $7^2 \times 2^2 \times 4^2$. Is your classmate correct?
Explain.

Answer _____

_____

LESSON 5.9 Using Order of Operations

New York Performance Indicators

6.N.22 Evaluate numerical expressions using order of operations (may include exponents of two and three)

6.PS.7 Represent problem situations verbally, numerically, algebraically, and/or graphically

6.PS.8 Select an appropriate representation of a problem

VOCABULARY

The **order of operations** gives the order in which operations should be performed when evaluating expressions.

REVIEW

Understanding Order of Operations

When given a mathematical expression that has several numbers and operations in it, everyone has to work the problem in the same way in order to get the same answer. The order of operations tells you which operations to perform first.

What You Should Know

When using the order of operations, you should perform the following steps in order:

1. Simplify the expressions within grouping symbols.
2. Find the value of all powers.
3. Multiply and divide in order from left to right.
4. Add and subtract in order from left to right.

Using Order of Operations

As you use order of operations to evaluate an expression, be sure to perform one operation at a time following the agreed upon steps.

EXAMPLE 1

Find the value of the expression.

$$17 - 10 + 2^3$$

You can evaluate the expression using order of operations.

There are three operations in the problem: subtract, add, and raise to a power. Order of operations tells you to find the value of the power first. Simplify the power using repeated multiplication. $2^3 = 2 \times 2 \times 2 = 8$

$$
\begin{aligned}
17 - 10 + 2^3 &= 17 - 10 + 8 && \text{Evaluate } 2^3. \\
&= 7 + 8 && \text{Subtract.} \\
&= 15 && \text{Add.}
\end{aligned}
$$

Understanding the Solution The solution is 15. The only way to get the correct solution is to perform the operations in the correct order. There are no parentheses in the problem, but there is a power. The power 2^3 should be found first, $2^3 = 8$. Of the remaining two operations (subtraction and addition), you should work from left to right. First subtract, $17 - 10 = 7$, and then add, $7 + 8 = 15$.

TRY IT!

Find the value of the expression.

$9 + 1^3 - 2 \times 3$

EXAMPLE 2

Simplify the expression $27 \div 3 \times (5 - 2) + 15$.

You can simplify the expression using order of operations.
According to order of operations, you should begin by performing the operation in the parentheses. $(5 - 2) = 3$

$27 \div 3 \times (5 - 2) + 15 = 27 \div 3 \times 3 + 15$	Simplify the expression within the parentheses.
$= 9 \times 3 + 15$	Divide.
$= 27 + 15$	Multiply.
$= 42$	Add.

Understanding the Solution The solution is 42. There are four operations in the problem; however, subtraction is done first because it is in parentheses: $(5 - 2) = 3$. Then the multiplication and division are performed from left to right in this order: $27 \div 3 = 9$, then $9 \times 3 = 27$. The addition is performed last: $27 + 15 = 42$.

TRY IT!

Simplify the expression $20 + (17 - 2) \div 5$.

EXAMPLE 3

Jake has \$45. He buys \$5 movie tickets for each of his 3 friends. Write an expression that shows how much money he has left. Evaluate your expression.

You can solve this problem by writing and simplifying an expression.
To write an expression, use the following.

$$\text{money Jake has} - \text{cost of 3 tickets}$$
$$45 \quad - \quad 3 \times 5$$

Use order of operations to find how much money he has left.

$$45 - 3 \times 5 = 45 - 15 \qquad \text{Multiply.}$$
$$= 30 \qquad \text{Subtract.}$$

▶ **Understanding the Solution**   Jake has $30 left. According to the order of operations, multiplication is done before subtraction.

TRY IT!

Amy has $160 in her savings account. For her birthday, she gets two $20 bills. She puts the money in her savings account. Write an expression showing how much money she will have in her savings. Then evaluate your expression to find the amount of money in her savings.

Exercises

SHORT RESPONSE

1 Simplify the expression.

$36 + 3^2 \div (6 - 3)$

Show your work.

Answer _____

2 Simplify the expression $48 - 5 + 7 \times 3$.

A 12

B 64

C 150

D 22

3 A dozen muffins costs \$5. Large bottles of juice cost \$2. Which expression could be used to find the cost of buying 3 dozen muffins and 4 large bottles of juice?

A 7×7

B $7 \times (5 + 2)$

C $3 \times 2 + 4 \times 5$

D $3 \times 5 + 4 \times 2$

4 Simplify the expression below.

$88 \div 4 + 7 \times (3 + 6)$

A 85

B 72

C 261

D 38

5 Which operation should you do first when evaluating the expression below?

$20 - 42 + (8 \div 2)$

A subtract

B multiply

C divide

D add

6 Simplify the expression $7 + (3^2 - 5) \times 7$.

A 35

B 14

C 77

D 56

7 Which operation should you do first when evaluating the expression below?

$12 + 6 \div 3 - 2 \times 4$

A add

B subtract

C multiply

D divide

8 $100 \div 5^2 \times (3 + 1)$

Part A

When evaluating this expression, which operation should you do first? Explain.

Show your work.

Answer _____

Part B

Find the value of the expression.

Show your work.

Answer _____

Estimating with Percents

New York Performance Indicators

6.N.26 Estimate a percent of quantity
6.PS.7 Represent problem situations verbally, numerically, algebraically, and/or graphically
6.PS.8 Select an appropriate representation of a problem
6.PS.5 Formulate problems and solutions from everyday situations

---

VOCABULARY

An **estimate** is an approximate amount, that is, a number close to the exact amount.

REVIEW

Understanding Estimating a Percent of a Number

Finding a percent of a number is the same as multiplying the number by a fraction that is equivalent to the percent. For example, finding 10% of 90 is the same as finding $\frac{1}{10} \times 90$.

To estimate the percent of a number, it is often helpful to find a simple fraction that is close in value to the given percent. Then multiply by the fraction instead of the percent. For example, to estimate 12% of 92, you know that 12% is close to 10% and 92 is close to 90.

$$\frac{1}{10} \times 90 = \frac{90}{10}$$
$$= 9$$

So, 12% of 92 is about 9.

What You Should Know

Below is list of some common percents and their fraction equivalents.

$10\% = \frac{1}{10}$ $20\% = \frac{1}{5}$ $30\% = \frac{3}{10}$

$40\% = \frac{2}{5}$ $50\% = \frac{1}{2}$ $60\% = \frac{3}{5}$

$70\% = \frac{7}{10}$ $80\% = \frac{4}{5}$ $90\% = \frac{9}{10}$

$25\% = \frac{1}{4}$ $75\% = \frac{3}{4}$

$33\frac{1}{3}\% = \frac{1}{3}$ $66\frac{2}{3}\% = \frac{2}{3}$

Estimating a Percent

Estimating a percent will give you an approximate answer. You want to work with numbers that are easy to work with. Some numbers many have to be rounded in order to do this.

EXAMPLE 1

Estimate 88% of 325.

You can estimate the answer by rounding the numbers in the problem.

Round 88% to 90%. Round 325 to 300. Since $90\% = \frac{9}{10}$, you can multiply.

$$\frac{9}{10} \times 300 = \frac{9 \times 300}{10}$$
$$= 270$$

Understanding the Solution   Is 88% of 325 approximately 270? Take the ratio of $\frac{270}{300}$ and divide both the numerator and denominator by 3. The equivalent fraction is $\frac{90}{100}$ which is 90%. 88% is approximately 90%.

TRY IT!

Estimate 42% of 79.

EXAMPLE 2

An ad in a newspaper has $39.96 calculators on sale for 25% off. About how much would you save by buying the calculator on sale?

You can estimate the answer by rounding the numbers in the problem.

Round $39.96 to $40. 25% is equivalent to the fraction $\frac{1}{4}$. Don't round 25% because 40 and $\frac{1}{4}$ are easily related to each other.

$$\frac{1}{4} \times 40 = \frac{40}{4}$$
$$= 10$$

Understanding the Solution   You would save approximately $10 by buying the calculator on sale. If you save $10, then you are saving $10 out of $39.96. $10 out of $40 simplifies to $\frac{1}{4}$. As a percent, $\frac{1}{4}$ is 25%.

TRY IT!

A clearance sale had 75% off of coat prices. A coat sells for $79.98. Approximately how much will you save by buying the coat on sale?

EXAMPLE 3

Estimate 49% of 5,970.

You can estimate the answer by rounding the numbers in the problem.

Round 49% to 50% or $\frac{1}{2}$. Round 5,970 to 6,000.

$$\frac{1}{2} \times 6,000 = 3,000$$

So, 49% of 5,970 is about 3,000.

Understanding the Solution   Since 49% is about $\frac{1}{2}$, and half or $\frac{1}{2}$ means to divide by 2, 6,000 ÷ 2 = 3,000.

TRY IT!

Estimate 23% of $43.

Exercises

1 Mr. Nguyen noticed 12% of his students did not turn in a book report. Out of the 27 students, approximately how many students did not turn in a book report?

Show your work.

Answer _____

MULTIPLE CHOICE

2 Estimate 26% of 47.

A 8
B 12
C 16
D 25

3 What number is about 34% of 59?

A 10
B 12
C 20
D 30

4 When asked if they had eaten breakfast that morning, 73% of the 28 students in a sixth grade class said that they had eaten breakfast. Approximately how many of the students ate breakfast that morning?

A 7 students
B 12 students
C 14 students
D 21 students

5 Ms. Cook has $385. She plans on spending 38% of the money on groceries. Approximately how much will she spend on groceries?

A $90
B $100
C $120
D $160

6 A family stops after traveling about 18% of the distance they want to travel. They want to travel 492 miles. Approximately how many miles have they traveled before stopping?

A 40 miles
B 80 miles
C 86 miles
D 100 miles

7 Your bill at a restaurant comes to $48. You want to leave a tip that is 20% of your bill. Approximately how much of a tip should you leave?

A $6
B $8
C $10
D $12

8 You can save 25% by buying a $79 bike while it is on sale.

PART A

Approximately how much money will you save by buying the bike on sale?
Show your work.

Answer _____

PART B

If you have $50 saved, will you have enough money to buy the bike? Explain.
Show your work.

Answer _____

Problem-Solving Strategy:
Reasonable Answers

 New York Performance Indicators
6.N.27 Justify the reasonableness of answers using estimation (including rounding)
6.PS.22 Discuss whether a solution is reasonable in the context of the original problem

Understand the Strategy

As you solve problems, you should look at the answer and think about whether it is reasonable given the size of the numbers in the problem. You might want to round the numbers and estimate the answer before working the problem. To be reasonable, the actual answer should be close to the estimated answer.

Problem: John sees a sign that says 25% off backpacks. He selects a backpack that costs $76. Is it reasonable for him to think he will save about $15? Explain.

SOLUTION

What do you know?   **What do you need to find?**

25% off price   Is $15 a reasonable amount to save?

Backpack costs $76

Find the relationship.

First estimate to find the amount that he could save by buying the backpack on sale. Round 76 to 80. $25\% = \frac{1}{4}$. Since $\frac{1}{4}$ and 80 are numbers that are easy to work with, don't round 25%. To find $\frac{1}{4}$ of 80, multiply.

$$\frac{1}{4} \times 80 = \frac{80}{4}$$
$$= 20$$

He will save approximately $20.

▶ **Understanding the Solution**   Yes, the estimated answer of $20 is larger than the actual savings because $76 was rounded up. He is going to save less than $20 and $15 < $20, so his estimate is reasonable.

1 While shopping for school supplies, a student picked out 2 packages of pencils for $0.99 each, 3 binders for $1.99 each, a lunch box for $9.89 and a backpack for $14.99. Will $30 cover the cost of the items he wants to buy? Explain.

Show your work.

Answer _____

_____

2 The sponsors of a run/walk expect to raise $50,000 from participants and donations. Each participant pays a $20 entry fee. There are 389 people who have signed up to participate in the run/walk. They received donations in the amount of $46,799. Is the amount they expect to raise reasonable? Explain.

Show your work.

Answer _____

_____

MULTIPLE CHOICE

1 Evaluate the expression.

$$64 - (44 - 30) \div 2 + 5^2$$

A 26

B 30

C 50

D 82

2 Kurt rides his bike $1\frac{3}{4}$ miles one week and $2\frac{2}{5}$ miles the next week. How many miles does he ride in two weeks?

A $3\frac{3}{20}$

B $3\frac{13}{20}$

C $4\frac{3}{20}$

D $4\frac{13}{20}$

3 Gwen spent $\frac{3}{8}$ of her homework time on math. Which decimal is equivalent to $\frac{3}{8}$?

A 0.38

B 2.6

C 0.375

D 0.125

4 Divide $1\frac{3}{4} \div 2\frac{1}{2}$.

A $\frac{7}{10}$

B $1\frac{1}{2}$

C $1\frac{3}{7}$

D $4\frac{3}{8}$

5 Your teacher asked the class to arrange these numbers in order.

$$-1 \quad 0.75 \quad -1.3 \quad -2$$

Which list shows the numbers in order from least to greatest?

A $-2 \quad -1.3 \quad -1 \quad 0.75$

B $0.75 \quad -1 \quad -1.3 \quad -2$

C $-1 \quad -1.3 \quad -2 \quad 0.75$

D $0.75 \quad -2 \quad -1.3 \quad -1$

6 Wendy said that her uncle is 4×3^2 years old. How old is her uncle?

A 14 years old

B 24 years old

C 36 years old

D 49 years old

7 Two brothers put their money together to buy a video game. One brother had $3.89 and the other $6.21.

Part A

Estimate the amount of money they have together.

Show your work.

Answer _____

Part B

Suppose a video game sells for $24.99. Do the two brothers have about 50% of the cost of the game? Explain.

Show your work.

Answer _____

8 Sam's goal was to walk $9\frac{1}{2}$ miles this week. The table below shows the number of miles she has walked so far.

Day	Distance (miles)
Monday	$1\frac{1}{2}$
Tuesday	$\frac{3}{4}$
Wednesday	$1\frac{5}{8}$
Thursday	$2\frac{3}{4}$

Part A

How far has she walked so far this week?

Show your work.

Answer _____

Part B

How far does she have to walk to meet her goal?

Show your work.

Answer _____

LESSON 6.1 Algebraic Expressions

New York Performance Indicators

6.A.1 Translate two-step verbal expressions into algebraic expressions

6.A.2 Use substitution to evaluate algebraic expressions with one variable (may include exponents of one, two and three)

6.PS.2 Understand that some ways of representing a problem are more efficient than others

6.PS.8 Select an appropriate representation of a problem

REVIEW

Understanding Algebraic Expressions

You can translate a verbal expression into an algebraic expression. The verbal expression "the sum of twice a number and 25" translates to the algebraic expression written below.

$$2x + 25$$

You can evaluate an expression by substituting a numerical value for the variable. Let $x = 5$, then replace the variable x with the value 5 and perform the operations.

$$2(5) + 25 = 10 + 25$$
$$= 35$$

Applying Algebraic Expressions

Admission to the fair costs $8. Each ride costs $3. Write an algebraic expression for the amount of money Melanie will spend at the fair on admission and rides. Then find the amount of money Melanie will spend if she rides 6 rides.

Let n represent the number of rides.

$$8 + 3n$$

To find the amount of money Melanie will need if she rides 6 rides, replace the variable n with 6.

$$8 + 3(6) = 8 + 18$$
$$= 26$$

Melanie will need $26.

Translating Verbal Expressions

You translate verbal expressions into algebraic expressions by relating the meaning of the words to numbers and operations.

EXAMPLE 1

Write an algebraic expression for the verbal expression "fifteen less half of a number."

You can solve this problem by translating the words into numbers, variables, and operations.

Look at each word or phrase and write a number or symbol.

fifteen less half of a number

15   − $\frac{1}{2}n$

Understanding the Solution   For the word *fifteen,* write the number 15. The word *less* means to subtract, so use the minus sign. To find one-half of a number, multiply the unknown number by one-half.

TRY IT!

Write an algebraic expression for the verbal expression "the difference of triple a number and 12."

Evaluating an Expression

You can evaluate an algebraic expression by substituting or replacing the variable with a given number or value.

EXAMPLE 2

Evaluate $9 + a^2$ for $a = 6$.

You can solve this problem by replacing the variable with the given number.

Replace a with 6. $9 + a^2$
$$9 + 6^2$$

Perform the operations using the order of operations. First evaluate the power, then find the sum.

$$9 + 6^2 = 9 + 36$$
$$= 45$$

Understanding the Solution   The order of operations tells us which operations to perform first.

> **Order of Operations**
> Evaluate expressions inside the grouping symbols.
> Evaluate all powers.
> Multiply and/or divide from left to right.
> Add and/or subtract from left to right.

Since there are no grouping symbols, evaluate the power: $6^2 = 36$.

Then perform the addition. $9 + 36 = 45$

TRY IT!

Evaluate $52 - b^2$ for $b = 7$.

EXAMPLE 3

At Pizza Plenty, Victoria orders 6 personal pizzas for her family and a pitcher of iced tea for $7. The total cost of the meal can be represented by the expression $6p + 7$. Find the cost of the meal if the personal pizzas cost $4 each.

You can solve this problem by evaluating the expression.
Evaluate the expression $6p + 7$ for $p = 4$.

Replace the variable p with the value 4.

$$6(4) + 7 = 24 + 7$$
$$= 31$$

▶ **Understanding the Solution**   In the expression $6p + 7$, $6p$ represents the cost of the 6 pizzas, and 7 represents the cost of the iced tea. Since the pizzas cost $4 each, the cost of the pizzas is 6 times $4, or $24. The total cost of the meal is the sum of $24 and $7, or $31.

TRY IT!

At the Beach Fun Shop, surfboards cost $5 per hour. A beach umbrella costs $12 for the day. Andrew rents a surfboard and an umbrella. The expression $5h + 12$ represents the total cost of the equipment. Find the total cost of the equipment if he returns the surfboard after 3 hours.

Exercises

SHORT RESPONSE

1 Alicia receives $100 for her birthday and uses the money to open a savings account. She plans to add $5 a month to her account. Write an algebraic expression to show the amount of money Alicia will have in her account after m months.

Show your work.

Answer _____

2 Which algebraic expression is a translation of the verbal expression "6 increased by double a number"?

A $6 \times 2 + n$

B $6 + 2n$

C $6 \div 2n$

D $6 \times 2 \times n$

3 Which is a verbal translation of the algebraic expression $3 \div n - 10$?

A three times a number less 10

B one-third of a number less 10

C the difference of a number divided by three and 10

D ten less than three divided by a number

4 Evaluate the expression $6x + 4$ for $x = 9$.

A 19

B 54

C 58

D 78

5 Evaluate the expression $x^3 - 7$ for $x = 5$.

A 8

B 18

C 118

D 125

6 Breanna plans to buy some notebooks for $3 each at BuyRite. She has $4 left on a gift card that she will use toward her purchases. If n is the number of notebooks Breanna buys, which algebraic expression shows the amount of money she needs?

A $7 + n$

B $3n$

C $3n + 4$

D $3n - 4$

7 Chelsea is on a vacation in Maine. She buys shell necklaces for n dollars each as gifts for three friends. If she pays for the necklaces with a $20 bill, then $20 - 3n$ is the amount of change Chelsea should receive. Find the amount of change she should receive if the necklaces cost $6 each.

A $2

B $14

C $18

D $26

8 Ari is planting a vegetable garden. He buys a pepper plant for $7 and a tomato plant for n dollars. At the checkout counter, the cashier tells him the tomato plant is half price. Which algebraic expression shows the amount of money Ari spent?

A $7 + 2n$

B $7 + \frac{1}{2}n$

C $2n - 7$

D $\frac{1}{2}n - 7$

9 The width of a patio is 5 feet less than the length.

Part A

Write an algebraic expression for the area of the patio. Indicate what the variable in the expression represents in your work.

Show your work.

Answer _____

Part B

If the length of the patio is 12 feet, what is the area of the patio?

Show your work.

Answer _____

Using Formulas

New York Performance Indicators

6.A.6 Evaluate formulas for given input values (circumference, area, volume, distance, temperature, interest, etc.)

6.PS.22 Discuss whether the solution is reasonable in the context of the original problem

6.CN.7 Apply mathematics to problem situations that develop outside of mathematics

6.CM.10 Use appropriate vocabulary when describing objects, relationships, mathematical solutions, and rationale

VOCABULARY

A **formula** is an equation that describes a relationship among two or more quantities.

REVIEW

Understanding Formulas

Below is a formula that can be used to find the temperature in degrees Celsius (C) when you know a temperature in degrees Fahrenheit (F).

$$C = \frac{5}{9} \times (F - 32)$$

You can evaluate the formula by substituting a numerical value for the variable F. Let $F = 59°$, then replace the variable F with the value 59 and perform the operations.

$$C = \frac{5}{9} \times (F - 32)$$

$$= \frac{5}{9} \times (59 - 32) \quad \text{Substitute.}$$

$$= \frac{5}{9} \times (27) \qquad \text{Subtract.}$$

$$= 15 \qquad\qquad \text{Multiply.}$$

So, a temperature of 59° Fahrenheit is equivalent to 15° Celsius.

Applying Formulas

Erika is planning a trip to France. She read that the average temperature in November in areas around Paris is about 10° Celsius. What is the average temperature in degrees Fahrenheit?

The formula $F = \left(\frac{9}{5} \times C\right) + 32$ can be used to convert degrees Celsius to degrees Fahrenheit. To find the temperature in degrees Fahrenheit, replace the variable C with 10.

$$F = \left(\frac{9}{5} \times C\right) + 32$$

$$= \left(\frac{9}{5} \times 10\right) + 32 \quad \text{Substitute.}$$

$$= 18 + 32 \qquad\qquad \text{Multiply.}$$

$$= 50 \qquad\qquad\qquad \text{Add.}$$

So, 10° Celsius is about 50° Fahrenheit.

Using Formulas

You can use formulas to solve many different types of problems, such as finding areas and volumes, determining the amount of interest on a bank account, or converting temperature between Fahrenheit and Celsius.

EXAMPLE 1

Find the area of a parallelogram with a base of 19 centimeters and a height of 6 centimeters. Use the formula $A = b \times h$, where b is the base and h is the height.

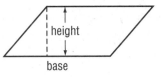

You can solve this problem by substituting the values for the base and the height into the formula.

$$A = b \times h$$
$$= 19 \times 6 \quad \text{Substitute.}$$
$$= 114 \quad\quad \text{Multiply.}$$

▶ **Understanding the Solution**   The area of the parallelogram is 114 square centimeters. You could also record the solution as 114 cm^2.

TRY IT!

The circumference of a circle is the distance around a circle. Find the circumference of a circle with a diameter of 5 inches using the formula $C = \pi d$, where d is the diameter. Let $\pi = 3.14$.

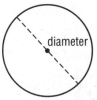

EXAMPLE 2

Marta rides her bicycle for 1.5 hours at a rate of 8 miles per hour. How far does she ride? Use the distance formula $d = r \times t$, where r is the rate and t is the time. Check your solution for reasonableness.

You can solve this problem by replacing the variable r with the given rate and the variable t with the time.

$$d = r \times t$$
$$= 8 \times 1.5 \quad \text{Substitute.}$$
$$= 12 \quad\quad\quad \text{Multiply.}$$

▶ **Understanding the Solution**   Look back at the problem to make sure the solution makes sense or is reasonable. The rate tells us that in 1 hour, Marta rides 8 miles, so in 2 hours she would ride twice that far, or 16 miles. The time 1.5 hours is more than 1 hour and less than 2 hours, so the solution should be between 8 and 16. The solution of 12 miles is reasonable since it is between 8 and 16.

TRY IT!

Ms. Brown drove her car at an average rate of 35 miles per hour for 3 hours. How far did she drive? Use the distance formula $d = r \times t$.

EXAMPLE 3

Roseanne opens a savings account with $250. The annual interest rate is 4%. How much simple interest will Roseanne earn after 5 years? Use the formula for simple interest: $I = p \times r \times t$, where p is the principal, r is the annual interest rate, and t is time in years.

You can solve this problem by replacing the variable p with the principal (the amount of money in the savings account), the variable r with the annual interest rate written as a decimal, and the variable t with the time in years.

$$I = p \times r \times t$$
$$= 250 \times 0.04 \times 5 \qquad \text{Substitute.}$$
$$= 50 \qquad \text{Multiply.}$$

▶ **Understanding the Solution**   Rosanne will earn $50 in interest after 5 years. To check that the solution is reasonable, consider how much interest she would earn in 1 year. It would be 4% of $250 or $10, so after 5 years it would 5 times that amount, or $50. The solution is reasonable.

TRY IT!

Mrs. Wilson loans her son Alex $1,000 for 2 years at a rate of 5% interest per year. How much will Alex owe his mother in interest after 2 years? Use the formula for simple interest $I = p \times r \times t$.

Exercises

SHORT RESPONSE

1 An aquarium has the dimensions 36 inches by 15 inches by 16 inches. Find its volume in cubic inches. Use the formula $V = \ell \times w \times h$, where ℓ is the length, w is the width, and h is the height of the aquarium.

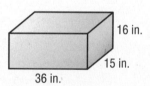

16 in.

15 in.

36 in.

Show your work.

Answer _____

2 A circular fishpond has a diameter of 10 feet. A fence will be put around the edge of the pond. How many feet of fencing are needed? Use the formula for the circumference of the circle, $C = \pi d$, where d is the diameter. Let $\pi = 3.14$.

A 10 feet

B 13.14 feet

C 31.04 feet

D 31.4 feet

3 A sheet of construction paper is 12 inches long and 9 inches wide. Use the area formula $A = \ell \times w$ to find the area of the paper.

A 21 square inches

B 96 square inches

C 108 square inches

D 129 square inches

4 Find the area of the triangle. Use the formula $A = \frac{1}{2} \times b \times h$, where b is the base and h is the height of the triangle.

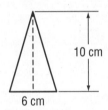

10 cm

6 cm

A 60 square centimeters

B 30 square centimeters

C 23 square centimeters

D 16 square centimeters

5 In Ryan's town the temperature is predicted to reach 45° Celsius. Use the following formula to find the temperature in degrees Fahrenheit:

$$F = \left(\frac{9}{5} \times C \right) + 32$$

A 53° Fahrenheit

B 57° Fahrenheit

C 77° Fahrenheit

D 113° Fahrenheit

6 Enrique flew on a jet airplane. The pilot said that the jet flew at an average speed of 624 miles per hour. The flight took 3.5 hours. How far did the plane fly? Use the distance formula $d = r \times t$ to help you find the answer.

A 218.4 miles

B 627.5 miles

C 2,184 miles

D 3,171 miles

7 Michael and Erin are training for a cross-country race. Michael jogs at a rate of 4 miles per hour for 2.5 hours. Erin jogs at a rate of 3.5 miles per hour for 4 hours. Who jogs farther? How much farther? Use the distance formula $d = r \times t$ to help you find the answer.

A Michael, 0.5 miles farther

B Erin, 4 miles farther

C Michael, 10 miles farther

D Erin, 14 miles farther

8 Mrs. Stiles used an installment plan to buy a television. On the installment plan, the television cost $900 plus 8% simple interest. She made 12 equal monthly payments for a year. Use the formula for simple interest $I = p \times r \times t$.

Part A

What was the amount of simple interest that Mrs. Stiles paid to buy the television on the installment plan?

Show your work.

Answer _____

Part B

What was the amount that Mrs. Stiles paid each month?

Show your work.

Answer _____

Problem-Solving Strategy: Relevant and Irrelevant Information

New York Performance Indicators
6.PS.1 Know the difference between relevant and irrelevant information when solving problems

Understand the Strategy

Sometimes problems have irrelevant information, or information that is not needed to solve the problems. It is important to identify the relevant information. The irrelevant or extra information can make the problem seem more complex or difficult than it really is.

Problem: Ms. Ortega left her office at 8:30 A.M. and drove straight to a client's office. She arrived there at 10:30 A.M. She drove at a rate of 28 miles per hour. She was with the client for 2 hours and 30 minutes. Then she returned to her office. Use the distance formula, $d = r \times t$ to find the distance from Ms. Ortega's office to her client's office.

SOLUTION

What do you know?

Left the office at 8:30 A.M.

Arrived at the client's office at 10:30 A.M.

Driving rate = 28 miles per hour

2 hours and 30 minutes with the client

Distance formula, $d = r \times t$

What do you need to find?

The number of miles to the client's office

Find the relationship.

To use the distance formula, you need to know the time and the rate. The problem gives three pieces of information involving time.

1. Left the office at 8:30 A.M.

2. Arrived at the client's office at 10:30 A.M.

3. 2 hours and 30 minutes with the client

The third piece of information is irrelevant to solving the problem. You only need the time she spent driving, not the amount of time she spent with the client. She drove from 8:30 A.M. to 10:30 A.M., or 2 hours.

Once you know the time and the rate, you can use the distance formula.

$$d = r \times t$$
$$= 28 \times 2 \qquad \text{Substitute.}$$
$$= 56 \qquad \text{Multiply.}$$

The client's office is 56 miles from Ms. Ortega's office.

▶ **Understanding the Solution**   You can check your solution by reviewing the problem and making sure you used the relevant information when finding your solution. The time traveling was relevant, and the time with the client was irrelevant.

Exercises

SHORT RESPONSE

1 Jessica wants to get a rug for her room. Her room is 10 feet by 12 feet. The rug she wants is 8 feet by 6 feet. Her mother prefers a rug that is 9 feet by 6 feet. Both rugs cost $2.50 per square foot. What area of Jessica's room floor would not be covered by the rug she wants? Report your answer in square feet.

Show your work.

Answer _____

2 Marcus is saving his money for a new guitar that costs $475. He works 6 hours a week at a horse stable and is paid $7 an hour. If he saves all that he earns, how much will he save in 6 weeks?

Show your work.

Answer _____

MULTIPLE CHOICE

1 Which algebraic expression is a translation of the verbal expression "forty more than a number divided by 3?"

A $\frac{n}{3} \times 40$

B $\frac{n}{3} + 40$

C $(40 - n) \div 3$

D $n + 40 + 3$

2 Evaluate the expression $29 + x^3$ for $x = 4$.

A 31

B 45

C 64

D 93

3 Sophie sells earrings at a craft show for $11 per pair. She has $15 at the start of the craft show. If p is the number of pairs of earrings she sells, $15 + 11p$ is the amount of money she will have at the end of the craft fair. Find the amount of money she will have if she sells 4 pairs of earrings.

A $26

B $44

C $59

D $165

4 Evan has a thermometer marked in degrees Celsius. The directions for a science experiment he is working on say to heat water to 176° Fahrenheit.

$$C = \frac{5}{9} \times (F - 32)$$

A 16° Celsius

B 29° Celsius

C 80° Celsius

D 115° Celsius

5 Which is a verbal translation of the algebraic expression $n^2 + 17$?

A seventeen more than double a number

B twice a number plus seventeen

C seventeen more than a number squared

D a number times two and seventeen more

6 Find the area of the circle below. Let $\pi = 3.14$.

$$A = \pi r^2$$

3 cm

A 9.42 square centimeters

B 18.84 square centimeters

C 28.26 square centimeters

D 88.7364 square centimeters

7 Rita is participating in a triathlon. She must swim, bike, and run. During the race she swims at the rate of 1 mile per hour. She bikes at a rate of 32 miles per hour and runs at a rate of 4 miles per hour. Use the distance formula: $d = r \times t$.

Part A

Rita swims 1 mile, then she bikes for $\frac{1}{2}$ hour. How many miles does she bike?

Show your work.

Answer _____

Part B

Rita completes the run in $\frac{3}{4}$ hour. How many miles long is the triathlon in all?

Show your work.

Answer _____

8 Matthew has $50. He buys some DVDs from a friend. Let n be the number of DVDs that Matthew buys.

Part A

Write an algebraic expression to show the amount of money Matthew has left if he buys the DVDs for $3 each.

Show your work.

Answer _____

Part B

What is the greatest number of DVDs that Matthew could buy and still have enough money left to buy a concert ticket for $25?

Show your work.

Answer _____

LESSON 7.1 Similar Triangles

New York Performance Indicators

6.G.1 Calculate the length of corresponding sides of similar triangles, using proportional reasoning

6.PS.11 Translate from a picture/diagram to a number or symbolic expression

6.CM.3 Organize and accurately label work

6.R.7 Use mathematics to show and understand physical phenomena (i.e., determine the perimeter of a bulletin board)

VOCABULARY

Similar triangles have the same shape but not necessarily the same size.

Congruent figures have the same size and shape.

The **corresponding sides** of similar triangles are the sides that match.

REVIEW

Understanding Similar Triangles

In the figures below, the measures of the angles are marked. The marks at $\angle B$ and $\angle E$ indicate right angles.

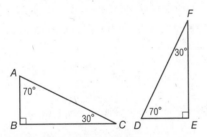

From looking at the figures, you know the following:

$\angle A$ corresponds to $\angle D$

$\angle B$ corresponds to $\angle E$

$\angle C$ corresponds to $\angle F$

$\overline{AB}$ corresponds to $\overline{DE}$

$\overline{BC}$ corresponds to $\overline{EF}$

$\overline{AC}$ corresponds to $\overline{DF}$

You also know that the ratios of the lengths of the corresponding sides are equal.

$$\frac{AB}{DE} = \frac{BC}{EF} = \frac{AC}{DF}$$

What You Should Know

- If the corresponding angles of two triangles are equal in measure, the triangles are similar.
- To identify corresponding angles, you must look at the figure for angle measurements or markings that indicate angles of equal measure. In the figure below, the corresponding angles are $\angle R$ and $\angle U$, $\angle S$ and $\angle V$, $\angle T$ and $\angle W$.

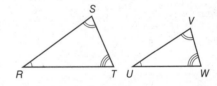

- In the statement $\triangle ABC \sim \triangle MNO$, the "$\sim$" indicates similarity and is read "is similar to."
- The statement $\triangle ABC \sim \triangle MNO$ tells you that the corresponding angles are $\angle A$ and $\angle M$, $\angle B$ and $\angle N$, and $\angle C$ and $\angle O$.

Writing a Proportion

When two triangles are similar, their corresponding sides are proportional, that is, they have a constant ratio. By identifying the corresponding sides of similar triangles, you can write a proportion.

EXAMPLE 1

In the figure below $\triangle RST \sim \triangle FGH$. Write a proportion that you could use to find the unknown length n.

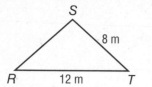 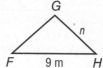

You can solve this problem by writing the ratios of the corresponding sides.
The three pairs of corresponding sides are $\overline{RS}$ and $\overline{FG}$, $\overline{ST}$ and $\overline{GH}$, and $\overline{RT}$ and $\overline{FH}$.

Since the two triangles are similar, you know that the ratios of the corresponding sides are equal. You can use this information to set up a proportion.

$$\frac{RT}{FH} = \frac{ST}{GH} \qquad \text{Write a proportion.}$$

$$\frac{12}{9} = \frac{8}{n} \qquad \text{Substitute.}$$

So the proportion that could be used to solve for n is $\frac{12}{9} = \frac{8}{n}$.

▶ **Understanding the Solution** The first ratio, $\frac{12}{9}$, compares the longest side of the first triangle to the longest side of the second triangle. The ratio $\frac{8}{n}$ compares the side of length 8 in the first triangle to the corresponding side of length n in the second triangle.

TRY IT!

In the figure below, the two triangles are similar. Write a proportion that you could use to find the unknown length.

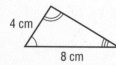 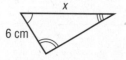

Finding a Missing Length

EXAMPLE 2

In the figure below, the triangles are similar. Find the missing measure x of the smaller triangle.

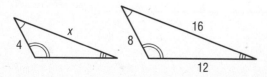

You can solve this problem by writing a proportion using the corresponding sides and solving for the unknown.

Since the side of length 4 corresponds to the side of length 8, and the side of length x corresponds to the side of length 16, you can write a proportion to find x.

$$\frac{4}{8} = \frac{x}{16}$$

To find the value of x, use the relationship between the two denominators, 8 and 16. Since $16 = 2 \times 8$, multiply both the numerator and denominator of $\frac{4}{8}$ by 2.

$$\frac{4 \times 2}{8 \times 2} = \frac{8}{16}$$

$$x = 8$$

So, the length of the unknown side is 8 units.

▶ **Understanding the Solution**   The triangles are similar, so the lengths of the sides of the triangles are proportional. It is important to match the sides in the proportion and to write them in the same order, 4 to 8 and x to 16. You can check your proportion by finding the product of the means and the product of the extremes.

Means: $8 \times 8 = 64$ Extremes: $4 \times 16 = 64$

So, $\frac{4}{8} = \frac{8}{16}$.

TRY IT!

Find the missing measure s.

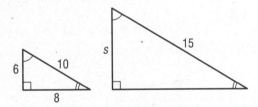

Exercises

SHORT RESPONSE

1 The two triangles are similar. What is the missing measure m?

Show your work.

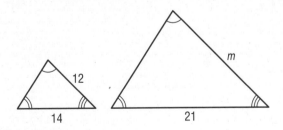

Answer _____

2 Which proportion could you use to find the missing measure *a* if the two triangles are similar?

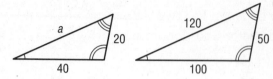

A $\frac{40}{100} = \frac{a}{120}$

B $\frac{20}{50} = \frac{a}{40}$

C $\frac{120}{a} = \frac{20}{50}$

D $\frac{a}{100} = \frac{40}{120}$

3 Triangle *DEF* is similar to triangle *JKL*. What is the missing measure *y*?

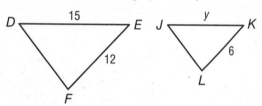

A 6.5

B 7.5

C 9

D 30

4 A flagpole is 20 feet tall and, in the afternoon, casts a shadow of 30 feet. At the same time, Keira casts a shadow of 7.5 feet. How tall is Keira?

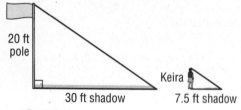

A 3 feet

B 4 feet

C 5 feet

D 10 feet

5 Which statement is not true about the two triangles below?

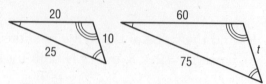

A The two triangles are similar.

B $\frac{20}{60} = \frac{25}{75}$

C $\frac{25}{75} = \frac{t}{10}$

D $\frac{20}{60} = \frac{10}{t}$

6 $\triangle RST : \triangle XYZ$. What is the value of *n*?

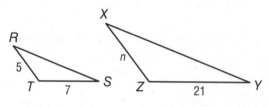

A 7

B 10

C 12

D 15

7 The two triangles are similar. What are the missing measures *x* and *y*?

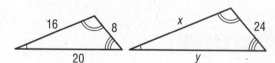

A $x = 4, y = 10$

B $x = 16, y = 60$

C $x = 48, y = 40$

D $x = 48, y = 60$

8 △*ABC* ~ △*LMN*.

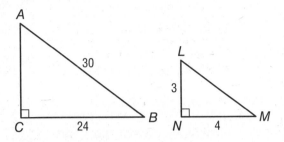

Part A

What is the length of $\overline{AC}$?

Show your work.

Answer _____

Part B

What is the length of $\overline{LM}$?

Show your work.

Answer _____

New York Performance Indicators

6.G.2 Determine the area of triangles and quadrilaterals (squares, rectangles, rhombi, and trapezoids) and develop formulas

6.PS.11 Translate from a picture/diagram to a number or symbolic expression

6.CM.3 Organize and accurately label work

6.RP.6 Develop and explain an argument verbally, numerically, algebraically, and/or graphically

VOCABULARY

A **rhombus** is a parallelogram with four congruent sides.

A **trapezoid** is a quadrilateral with exactly one pair of parallel sides.

REVIEW

Understanding Finding Area

You can use formulas to find the areas of quadrilaterals. The formulas for the area of a parallelogram, rectangle, square, and rhombus are given below:

Parallelogram

$A = b \times h$, where b is the base and h is the height.

Rectangle

$A = \ell \times w$, where ℓ is the length and w is the width.

Square

$A = s^2$, where s is the length of one side.

Rhombus

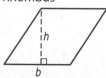

$A = b \times h$, where b is the base and h is the height.

What You Should Know

You can use the formula for the area of a parallellogram to help you develop a formula for the area of a triangle.

Any triangle with a base b and a height h can be thought of as half of a parallelogram with a base b and a height h. The area of the parallelogram is $b \times h$.

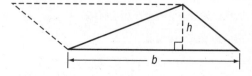

The area of the triangle is half the area of a parallelogram. So the formula for the area of a triangle is $A = \frac{1}{2} bh$.

The formula for the area of a trapezoid is $A = \frac{1}{2} (b_1 + b_2)h$, where b_1 and b_2 are the bases of the trapezoid and h is the height.

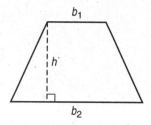

Areas of Quadrilaterals

To find the areas of quadrilaterals such as parallelograms, rhombi, rectangles, squares, and trapezoids, you can use the appropriate formulas. It is important to always report the area of any figure in square units.

EXAMPLE 1

Find the area of the rhombus.

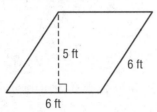

A rhombus is a parallelogram that has all sides the same length. You can solve this problem by using the formula for the area of a parallelogram $A = b \times h$.

$$A = b \times h$$
$$= 6 \times 5$$
$$= 30$$

The area of the rhombus is 30 square feet, or 30 ft².

▶ Understanding the Solution   Even though the sides of a rhombus are equal in length like in a square, you must multiply one of the sides called the base by the height to find the area rather than multiplying $s \times s$ like in a square.

TRY IT!

Find the area of the rhombus with sides of length 17 meters and a height of 25 meters.

EXAMPLE 2

Find the area of the trapezoid.

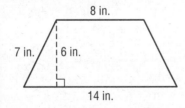

You can solve this problem by using the formula for the area of a trapezoid.

$$A = \frac{1}{2}(b_1 + b_2)h$$

In this formula b_1 and b_2 represent the lengths of the bases, which are the two parallel sides.

$$A = \frac{1}{2}(b_1 + b_2)h = \frac{1}{2} \times (8 + 14) \times 6 \qquad \text{Substitute.}$$

$$= \frac{1}{2} \times 22 \times 6 \qquad\qquad\qquad \text{Add.}$$

$$= 66 \qquad\qquad\qquad\qquad \text{Multiply.}$$

The area of the trapezoid is 66 square inches or 66 in^2.

▶ **Understanding the Solution** The bases of this trapezoid are 8 inches and 14 inches. To find the area of the trapezoid, the formula uses the height and the average of the two bases, or $\frac{1}{2}(b_1 + b_2)$.

TRY IT!

The lengths of the parallel sides of a trapezoid are 15 centimeters and 21 centimeters. If its height is 8 centimeters, what is its area?

Areas of Triangles

EXAMPLE 3

Find the area of the triangle.

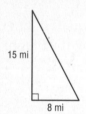

15 mi

8 mi

You can solve this problem by using the formula for the area of a triangle.

$$A = \frac{1}{2}b \times h$$

$$= \frac{1}{2}(8) \times 15$$

$$= 4 \times 15$$

$$= 60$$

The area of the triangle is 60 square miles.

▶ **Understanding the Solution** In a right triangle, the base of the triangle is one of the sides that forms that right angle, and the height is the other.

TRY IT!

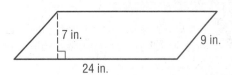

65 mm · 40 mm · 52 mm

Find the area of the triangle.

Exercises

SHORT RESPONSE

1 What is the area of the parallelogram?

Show your work.

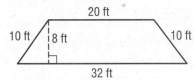

7 in. · 9 in. · 24 in.

Answer _____

MULTIPLE CHOICE

2 Erik is running for class president. He uses a rectangular piece of poster board to make a sign. What is the area of his sign?

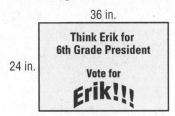

36 in.

24 in.

Think Erik for
6th Grade President

Vote for

Erik!!!

A 864 square inches
B 432 square inches
C 120 square inches
D 60 square inches

3 Jena made a triangular pennant for her gymnastics team. The base of the pennant is 6 inches and the height of the pennant is 14 inches. What is the area of the pennant?

A 20 square inches
B 36 square inches
C 42 square inches
D 84 square inches

4 The ecology club has a garden that is in the shape of a trapezoid. What is the area of the garden?

20 ft

10 ft · 8 ft · 10 ft

32 ft

A 91 square feet
B 104 square feet
C 182 square feet
D 208 square feet

5 What is the area of the figure shown?

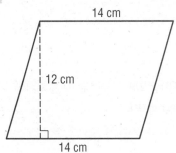

14 cm

12 cm

14 cm

A 56 square centimeters
B 68 square centimeters
C 168 square centimeters
D 196 square centimeters

6 What is the area of the triangle?

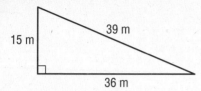

15 m

39 m

36 m

A 585 square meters
B 540 square meters
C 294 square meters
D 270 square meters

7 What is the area of the parallelogram?

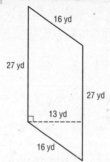

16 yd

27 yd

27 yd

13 yd

16 yd

A 351 square yards
B 432 square yards
C 208 square yards
D 86 square yards

EXTENDED RESPONSE

8 A square pool has a triangular platform in the center. The pool measures 5 meters on a side. The base of the triangular platform is 2 meters long and its height is 1 meter.

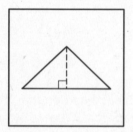

Part A

What is the area of the pool that is covered by the triangular platform?
Show your work.

Answer _____

Part B

What is the area of the pool that is not covered by the triangular platform?
Show your work.

Answer _____

LESSON 7.3 | # Finding Area of Regular and Irregular Polygons

 New York Performance Indicators

6.G.3 Use a variety of strategies to find the area of regular and irregular polygons

6.PS.11 Translate from a picture/diagram to a number or symbolic expression

6.CM.2 Explain a rationale for strategy selection

6.R.7 Use mathematics to show and understand physical phenomena (i.e., determine the perimeter of a bulletin board)

VOCABULARY

A **polygon** is a simple closed plane figure formed by three or more line segments.

A **regular polygon** is a polygon that has all sides congruent and all angles congruent.

REVIEW

Understanding Regular and Irregular Polygons

- All of the sides of an equilateral polygon are equal in measure.
- All of the angles of an equilateral polygon are equal in measure.
- Regular polygons are both equilateral and equiangular.

A square is an example of a regular polygon since all of its sides are the same length and all of its angles are right angles.

It is possible for a polygon to be equilateral but not equiangular.

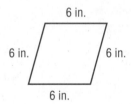

It is also possible for a polygon to be equiangular but not equilateral.

Polygons that are not regular are sometimes referred to as *irregular* polygons.

Applying Strategies

When finding the area of an irregular polygon, you may need to
- break the figure into smaller parts,
- find the areas of the parts,
- and add the areas together to find the total area.

For example, this L-shaped polygon can be separated into two quadrilaterals.

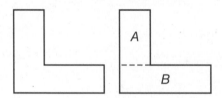

The total area of the polygon is equal to the area of polygon *A* plus the area of polygon *B*.

Finding the Areas of Polygons

To find the areas of regular polygons, such as equilateral triangles and squares, you can use the area formulas that you know. You can use other strategies such as breaking apart, drawing a diagram, or taking away a section to find the areas of polygons for which you do not have a formula.

EXAMPLE 1

Find the area of the polygon.

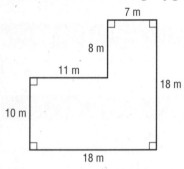

You can think of the figure as a large square with a small rectangle taken away from it. To help you see the square, add dotted lines to the diagram. The square is 18 meters on a side. Use the formula to find the area of the square.

$$A = s^2$$
$$A = 18 \times 18 = 324$$

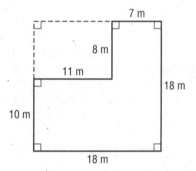

The small rectangle is 8 meters by 11 meters. Use the formula to find the area of the rectangle.

$$A = \ell \times w$$
$$A = 8 \times 11 = 88$$

Now find the difference between the area of the square and the area of the rectangle.

$$324 - 88 = 236$$

▶ **Understanding the Solution**   The area of the polygon is 236 square feet or 236 ft². There is no formula for the area of an irregular polygon such as the one shown, but by thinking of the figure as a square with a missing rectangle, you can use the difference of two areas to find the area of the figure.

TRY IT!

Find the area of the polygon.

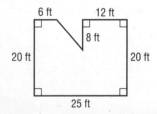

EXAMPLE 2

Find the area of the polygon.

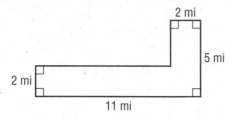

You can solve this problem by separating the figure into two rectangles.
The polygon can be broken into two rectangles, A and B.

Rectangle A is 2 miles by 3 miles.
Rectangle B is 2 miles by 11 miles.

The area of rectangle *A* is 2 × 3 = 6.
The area of rectangle *B* is 2 × 11 = 22.

The area of the polygon is the sum of the areas
of the two rectangles.

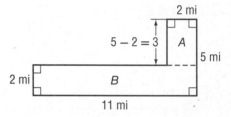

$$6 + 22 = 28$$

▶ **Understanding the Solution**   The area of the polygon is 28 square miles or 28 mi².
It is equal to the sum of the areas of the two rectangles. Sometimes not all the
dimensions are explicitly given. In this case, to determine the vertical length of
Rectangle *A* it is necessary to think 5 − 2 = 3.

TRY IT!

Find the area of the polygon.

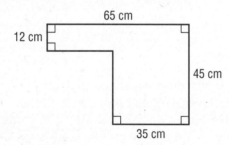

Exercises

SHORT RESPONSE

1 What is the area of the polygon? (Hint: Break the figure
apart into a triangle and a trapezoid.)

  Show your work.

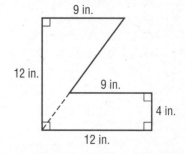

Answer _____

2 Luis is creating a rectangular trivet 30 centimeters by 15 centimeters using small square tiles with sides of length 3 centimeters. The corners of the trivet will each have a square red tile. The rest of the tiles will be black. How many black tiles will he need?

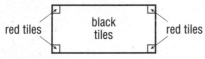

red tiles   black tiles   red tiles

A 45 tiles
B 46 tiles
C 446 tiles
D 450 tiles

3 An herb garden is planted in the shape of an isosceles triangle. It has a base of 6 yards and a height of 4 yards. What is the area of the garden?

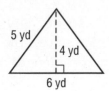

5 yd   4 yd   6 yd

A 10 square yards
B 12 square yards
C 24 square yards
D 20 square yards

4 What is the area of the polygon?

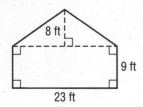

8 ft   9 ft   23 ft

A 184 square feet
B 207 square feet
C 299 square feet
D 391 square feet

5 Which strategy could not be used find the area of the polygon?

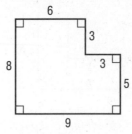

6   3   8   3   5   9

A Add the areas of an 8 by 6 rectangle and a 5 by 3 rectangle.
B Subtract the area of a 3 by 3 square from the area of an 8 by 8 square.
C Subtract the area of a 3 by 3 square from the area of a 9 by 8 rectangle.
D Add the areas of a 5 by 9 rectangle and a 3 by 6 rectangle.

6 What is the area of the polygon?

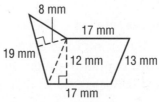

8 mm   17 mm   19 mm   12 mm   13 mm   17 mm

A 280 square millimeters
B 373 square millimeters
C 419 square millimeters
D 1,632 square millimeters

7 Alec describes the shape of a flower garden as a regular polygon with four sides. Each side has a length of 15 yards. There is a diagonal path across the garden that is 21 yards long. What is the area of the garden?

A 72 square yards
B 225 square yards
C 315 square yards
D 441 square yards

8 Bettina is using gold fabric and red fabric to make a decorative tablecloth in the shape of an irregular octagon.

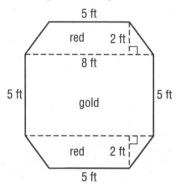

Part A

What is the total area of the tablecloth?

Show your work.

Answer _____

Part B

Is more of the tablecloth red or gold? How much more?

Show your work.

Answer _____

LESSON 7.4 Finding Volume of Rectangular Prisms

New York Performance Indicators

6.G.4 Determine the volume of rectangular prisms by counting cubes and develop the formula

6.PS.6 Translate from a picture/diagram to a numeric expression

6.PS.12 Use trial and error and the process of elimination to solve problems

VOCABULARY

Volume is the number of cubic units needed to fill the space occupied by a solid figure.

A **rectangular prism** is a solid figure that has two parallel and congruent bases that are rectangles.

REVIEW·

Understanding Finding Volume of Rectangular Prisms

The amount of space inside a three-dimensional object is called volume. Volume is measured in cubic units.

You can find the volume by counting the number of unit cubes it takes to fill the object. For example, this rectangular prism holds 72 unit cubes. So its volume is 72 cubic units.

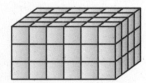

What You Should Know

When counting the number of unit cubes to find the volume of a rectangular prism, first find the number of cubes in one layer by multiplying the number of cubes along the length by the number of cubes along the width. Then multiply the number of cubes in that layer by the number of layers.

You are basically multiplying the length by the width by the height.

The volume of any rectangular prism can be found using the formula $V = \ell w h$, where ℓ is length, w is width, and h is height.

Finding Volume by Counting Cubes

Since the volume of a rectangular prism is the number of unit cubes it takes to fill the prism, one way to find the volume is to count the cubes.

EXAMPLE 1

Find the volume of the prism.

You can solve this problem by counting the cubes inside the prism. Don't forget to count the cubes you cannot see.

The top layer has 24 cubes. There are three layers of 24 each, so there are 72 cubes in all.

▶ **Understanding the Solution**   The volume of the prism is 72 cubic units. When counting the number of unit cubes, first find the number of cubes in one layer, and then multiply the number of cubes in that layer by the number of layers.

TRY IT!

Find the volume of the prism.

Finding Volume Using a Formula

You can also find the volume of a rectangular prism by using a formula.

EXAMPLE 2

Use the formula to find the volume of the prism.

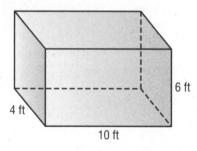

You can solve this problem using the formula V = ℓwh.

The length of the prism is 10 feet.
The width of the prism is 4 feet.
The height of the prism is 6 feet.
Substitute those values into the formula $V = ℓwh$.

$$= (10)(4)(6)$$
$$= 240 \text{ cubic feet}$$

▶ **Understanding the Solution**   The volume of the rectangular prism is 240 cubic feet, or 240 ft³. That means that 240 1-foot by 1-foot by 1-foot cubes could fit into this prism.

TRY IT!

Use the formula to find the volume of the prism that is 5 centimeters long, 4 centimeters wide, and 8 centimeters high.

Exercises

1 What is an example of a real world object that has a volume between 150 and 400 cubic inches?

Show your work.

Answer _____

2 What is the volume of the rectangular prism?

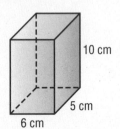

10 cm

5 cm

6 cm

A 10 cubic centimeters
B 30 cubic centimeters
C 110 cubic centimeters
D 300 cubic centimeters

3 What is the volume of a rectangular prism that is 10 meters long, 2 meters wide, and 11 meters high?

A 42 cubic meters
B 132 cubic meters
C 220 cubic meters
D 240 cubic meters

4 A lunch box is 5 inches long, 4 inches wide, and 12 inches high. What is the volume of the lunch box?

A 220 cubic inches
B 240 cubic inches
C 260 cubic inches
D 280 cubic inches

5 A fish tank is 36 inches long, 19 inches wide, and 23 inches high. What is the volume of the tank?

A 469 cubic inches
B 707 cubic inches
C 13,984 cubic inches
D 15,732 cubic inches

6 The volume of a rectangular prism is 36 cubic meters. The length of the prism is 6 meters and the width is 3 meters. What is the height of the prism?

A 1 meter
B 2 meters
C 3 meters
D 4 meters

7 Which rectangular prism has a volume of 126 cubic inches?

A
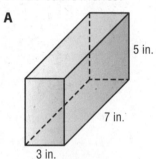
5 in.
7 in.
3 in.

B
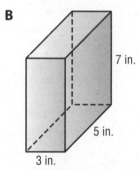
7 in.
5 in.
3 in.

C
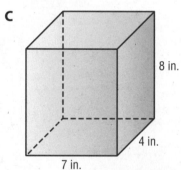
8 in.
4 in.
7 in.

D
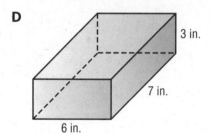
3 in.
7 in.
6 in.

8 Which rectangular prism has a volume of 72 cubic yards?

A
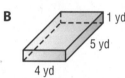
9 yd
2 yd
4 yd

B
1 yd
5 yd
4 yd

C
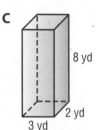
8 yd
2 yd
3 yd

D
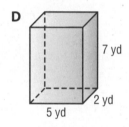
7 yd
2 yd
5 yd

9 The volume of a rectangular prism is 154 cubic feet. The width of the prism is 7 feet and the height is 2 feet. What is the length of the prism in feet?

A 7
B 10
C 11
D 15

10 Use the prism below to answer parts A and B.

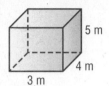

5 m
4 m
3 m

Part A

What is the volume of the prism?

Show your work.

Answer _____

Part B

Draw a different rectangular prism that has the same volume as the prism above.

Show your work.

Answer _____

LESSON 7.5 — *Problem-Solving Strategy: Drawing a Diagram*

New York Performance Indicators

6.PS.6 Translate from a picture/diagram to a numeric expression

6.PS.7 Represent problem situations verbally, numerically, algebraically, and/or graphically

6.PS.11 Translate from a picture/diagram to a number or symbolic expression

Understand the Strategy

When solving word problems, sometimes it can be helpful to draw a diagram. Diagrams are good ways to visualize information.

Problem: Find the volume of a rectangular prism that has a length of 8 inches, a width of 3 inches, and a height that is half the length.

SOLUTION

What do you know?

The rectangular prism is 8 inches long.

It is 3 inches wide.

Its height is half its length.

What do you need to find?

The volume of the rectangular prism

Find the relationship.

A diagram might help you to visualize the rectangular prism, so make a sketch. You can label the length 8 inches and the width 3 inches. In order to label the height, you must calculate one-half the length.

$$\frac{1}{2} \times 8 = 4$$

So label the height 4 inches.

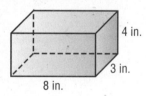

4 in.

3 in.

8 in.

Now you can find the volume by multiplying the length by the width by the height.

$$V = \ell wh$$
$$= (8)(3)(4)$$
$$= 96$$

So the volume of the rectangular prism is 96 cubic inches.

▶ **Understanding the Solution** Drawing and labeling a figure can help you find the volume of the rectangular prism. Before the labeling takes place, all dimensions must be found. The height had to be calculated. Once it was known, the length, width, and height could be labeled and used in the formula to calculate the volume.

Exercises

1 Find the volume of a rectangular prism that has a length of 9 centimeters, a width of 2 centimeters, and a height of 10 centimeters.

Show your work.

Answer _____

2 A rectangular prism has a volume of 120 cubic meters. The length is 6 meters and the width is 4 meters. What is the height of the prism?

Show your work.

Answer _____

LESSON 7.6 Circles

New York Performance Indicators

6.G.5   Identify radius, diameter, chords and central angle of a circle

6.G.9   Understand the relationship between the diameter and the radius of the circle

6.PS.13 Model problems with pictures/diagrams or physical objects

VOCABULARY

The **radius** of a circle is a line segment that connects the center of a circle to a point on the circle or the length of that segment.

A **chord** is a line segment that connects two points on a circle.

The **diameter** of a circle is a chord that passes through the center of the circle or the length of that chord.

A **central angle** is an angle whose vertex is the center of the circle.

REVIEW

Understanding Circles

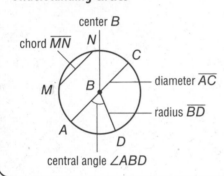

center B

chord $\overline{MN}$

diameter $\overline{AC}$

radius $\overline{BD}$

central angle $\angle ABD$

What You Should Know

The radius of a circle is half the length of the diameter, so

$$r = \frac{d}{2} \quad \text{and} \quad d = 2r$$

Identifying the Parts of a Circle

The information in the review sections above can be used to help you identify the parts of a circle.

EXAMPLE 1

Identify the radii, the diameter, a chord, and a central angle on the circle below.

You can solve this problem using the vocabulary list at the top of the page.

Look at the circle.

List any radii you can identify. $\overline{RQ}, \overline{RS}, \overline{RT}, \overline{RU}$

List any diameters you can identify. $\overline{QU}$

List any chords you can identify. $\overline{QU}$

List any central angles you can identify. $\angle QRS, \angle SRT, \angle TRU, \angle SRU,$
                                                    $\angle QRT, \angle QRU$

▶ **Understanding the Solution**   There are 4 radii, 1 diameter, 1 chord, and 6 central angles on this circle.

TRY IT!

Draw a circle. Label the center *I*. Draw diameter $\overline{GH}$. Draw a radius $\overline{IF}$. Name one central angle on the circle you drew.

Calculating the Lengths of Radii and Diameters

EXAMPLE 2

Find the diameter of a circle with a radius of 5 centimeters.

You can solve this problem by using the formula $d = 2r$.
The length of the diameter is twice the length of the radius.

$\qquad d = 2r$
$\qquad\quad = 2(5)$ Substitute.
$\qquad\quad = 10$ Multiply.

▶ **Understanding the Solution**   The length of the diameter is 10 centimeters, twice the length of the radius.

TRY IT!

Find the radius of a circle with a diameter of 18 feet.

Exercises

SHORT RESPONSE

1 Is a diameter always a chord? Defend your answer.

Show your work.

Answer _____

_____

_____

_____

MULTIPLE CHOICE

Use the following figure for Exercises 2 and 3.

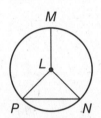

2 Which of the following is not a central angle?

A ∠MLN

B ∠NLP

C ∠PLM

D ∠LPN

3 Which of the following is not a radius?

A $\overline{ML}$

B $\overline{PN}$

C $\overline{LN}$

D $\overline{PL}$

4 If the diameter of a circle is 48 meters, what is the measure of the radius?

A 4 meters

B 12 meters

C 24 meters

D 96 meters

5 If the diameter of a circle is 102 centimeters, what is the measure of the radius?

A 2 centimeters

B 51 centimeters

C 95 centimeters

D 204 centimeters

6 If the radius of a circle is 12 meters, what is the measure of the diameter?

A 4 meters

B 6 meters

C 20 meters

D 24 meters

7 If the radius of a circle is 25 inches, what is the measure of the diameter?

A 5 inches

B 12.5 inches

C 50 inches

D 75 inches

EXTENDED RESPONSE

8 Draw a circle. Label the center *X*. Draw a central angle and label it $\angle YXZ$. Draw a diameter $\overline{WV}$.

Part A

Show your work.

Answer ________________

Part B

If the measure of $\overline{WX}$ is 15 centimeters, how long is $\overline{WV}$?

Show your work.

Answer ________________

LESSON 7.7 Area and Circumference of Circles

New York Performance Indicators

6.G.7 Determine the area and circumference of a circle, using the appropriate formula

6.G.9 Understand the relationship between the circumference and the diameter of a circle

6.PS.23 Verify results of a problem

VOCABULARY

The **circumference** of a circle is the distance, also known as the length, around a circle.

REVIEW

Understanding Area and Circumference of Circles

The circumference of a circle is the distance around the circle.

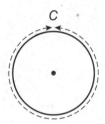

What You Should Know

- Pi is an irrational number whose value is 3.1415926....
- The diameter of a circle is twice the length of the radius.
- The circumference of a circle is π times the length of its diameter or π times twice the length of its radius.

$$C = \pi d \qquad \text{or} \qquad C = 2\pi r$$

- The area of a circle is π times the square of the length of its radius.

$$A = \pi r^2$$

Finding the Circumference of a Circle

Circumference of a circle is a little more than three times the length of its diameter. This is good to know when checking to see if your answer is reasonable.

EXAMPLE 1

Find the circumference of a circle that has a diameter of 5 inches. Use 3.14 for π.

You can solve this problem using the formula C = πd.

$$
\begin{aligned}
C &= \pi d \\
&= 3.14 \times 5 \quad \text{Substitute.} \\
&= 15.7 \quad\quad\ \text{Multiply.}
\end{aligned}
$$

Understanding the Solution   The circumference of the circle is 15.7 inches. The diameter is 5 inches and the circumference should be a little more than three times the diameter. So 15.7 inches is a reasonable answer.

TRY IT!

Find the circumference of a circle that has a diameter of 9 feet. Use 3.14 for π.

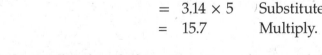

EXAMPLE 2

Use a calculator to find the circumference of a circle that has a radius of 12 meters. Use 3.14 for π.

You can solve this problem using the formula $C = 2\pi r$.

$$
\begin{aligned}
C &= 2\pi r \\
&= 2 \times 3.14 \times 12 \quad \text{Substitute.} \\
&= 75.36 \quad\quad\quad\quad\; \text{Multiply.}
\end{aligned}
$$

▶ **Understanding the Solution**   The circumference of the circle is 75.36 meters. The diameter is 24 meters, and the circumference should be a little more than three times the diameter. So a circumference of 75.36 meters is a reasonable answer.

TRY IT!

Use a calculator to find the circumference of a circle that has a radius of 2 yards. Use 3.14 for π.

Finding the Area of a Circle

The area of a circle can be found using the formula $A = \pi r^2$.

EXAMPLE 3

Find the area of a circle that has a radius of 4 inches. Use 3.14 for π.

You can solve this problem using the formula $A = \pi r^2$.

$$
\begin{aligned}
A &= \pi r^2 \\
&= 3.14 \times 4^2 \quad \text{Substitute.} \\
&= 3.14 \times 16 \quad \text{Evaluate the power.} \\
&= 50.24 \quad\quad\;\; \text{Multiply.}
\end{aligned}
$$

▶ **Understanding the Solution**   The area of the circle is 50.24 square inches. To use the formula $A = \pi r^2$, you must know the length of the radius. If the diameter is given in the problem, divide it by 2 to calculate the radius before using the formula. Also, remember that area is always written in square units.

TRY IT!

Find the area of a circle that has a diameter of 10 centimeters. Use 3.14 for π.

Exercises

1 What is the circumference of the circle below? Use 3.14 for π.

Show your work.

Answer _____

MULTIPLE CHOICE

2 Which is a good estimate for the circumference of a circle with a diameter of 12 feet?

A 3 feet

B 6 feet

C 24 feet

D 36 feet

3 Which is a good estimate for the circumference of a circle with a radius of 7 meters?

A 3.5 meters

B 14 meters

C 21 meters

D 42 meters

4 What is the circumference of a circle with a diameter of 20 centimeters? Use 3.14 for π.

A 31.4 centimeters

B 62.8 centimeters

C 125.6 centimeters

D 188.4 centimeters

5 What is the circumference of a circle with a radius of 11 millimeters? Use 3.14 for π.

A 5.5 millimeters

B 22 millimeters

C 69.08 millimeters

D 379.94 millimeters

6 What is the area of a circle with a radius of 6 miles? Use 3.14 for π.

A 18.84 square miles

B 37.68 square miles

C 113.04 square miles

D 452.16 square miles

7 What is the area of a circle with a diameter of 14 meters? Use 3.14 for π.

A 43.96 square meters

B 87.92 square meters

C 153.86 square meters

D 615.44 square meters

8 The diameter of a manhole cover is 26 inches. What is its circumference? Use 3.14 for π.

Part A
Show your work.

Answer _____

Part B
What is the area of the cover?
Show your work.

Answer _____

Finding the Area of a Sector

VOCABULARY

An **arc** of a circle is a part of the circle.

A **sector** is a part of a circle bounded by two radii and an arc.

REVIEW

Understanding Area of a Sector

It is important to know that a sector of a circle is a fractional part of the whole circle, and that the sum of the central angles of a circle is 360°.

In the figure below, the measure of the central angle of the sector is 90°. The circle has a radius of 8 centimeters.

To find the area of the sector, multiply the fractional part of the circle by the area of the circle.

$$A = \frac{90}{360} \times \pi r^2$$

$$= \frac{1}{4} \times \pi \times 8^2$$

$$= 16\pi$$

So the exact area of the circle in terms of π is 16π square centimeters

What You Should Know

- A *radius* of a circle is a line segment that connects the center of a circle to a point on the circle.
- The area of a circle can be found using the formula $A = \pi r^2$.
- Pi (π) is an irrational number. So it does not have an exact numerical value.
- To indicate the exact value for the area of a circle, leave the area in terms of π. For example, the area of the circle in the example was exactly 16π.
- To find an approximate area of a circle, you can substitute the decimal 3.14 or the fraction $\frac{22}{7}$ for π. So 16π is approximately 16×3.14 or about 50.24.

Finding the Part of a Circle When Given the Measure of a Central Angle

The sum of the measures of the central angles of a circle is 360°. A sector is a fractional part of the whole circle. To determine what fractional part of the circle the sector is, write the ratio of the measure of the central angle of the sector to 360° and write the ratio as a fraction or decimal.

EXAMPLE 1

What part of a circle is a sector with a central angle that measures 18°?

You can express the angle as a fractional part of 360° to solve this problem.

Write the ratio of the measure of the central angle of the sector to 360° as a fraction. Then simplify.

$$\frac{18}{360} = \frac{1}{20}$$

To express $\frac{1}{20}$ as a decimal, divide 1 by 20.

$$\frac{1}{20} = 0.05$$

So the sector of the circle is $\frac{1}{20}$ or 0.05 of the circle.

▶ **Understanding the Solution** A sector of a circle is part of the whole circle. In this problem, it is 18° out of 360°. So the sector is $\frac{18}{360} = \frac{1}{20}$ of the circle. Expressed as a decimal, the sector is 0.05 of the circle.

TRY IT!

What part of a circle is a sector with a central angle of 99°? Give the answer as a simplified fraction and in decimal form.

Finding the Area of a Sector

The area of a sector is a fractional part of the whole area of the circle. To find the area of the sector, multiply the fractional part of the circle by the area of the circle. You can also use the formula

$$A = \frac{\text{central angle}}{360} \times \pi r^2.$$

EXAMPLE 2

A pizza has a radius of 9 inches. The pizza is divided into sections. One of the sections has a central angle with a measure of 60°. What is the area of this section of pizza? Use $\pi = 3.14$.

You can solve this problem by finding the area of a sector of a circle.

Use the formula $A = \dfrac{\text{central angle}}{360} \times \pi r^2$.

$$A = \frac{\text{central angle}}{360} \times \pi r^2$$

$$= \frac{60}{360} \times 3.14 \times 9^2 \qquad \text{Substitute.}$$

$$= \frac{1}{6} \times 3.14 \times 9^2 \qquad \text{Simplify } \frac{60}{360}.$$

$$= \frac{254.34}{6} \qquad \text{Multiply.}$$

$$= 42.39 \text{ square inches} \qquad \text{Divide.}$$

▶ **Understanding the Solution** One piece of pizza is part of the whole pizza. In this case, $\frac{60}{360} = \frac{1}{6}$ of the pizza. The area of the whole pizza is 3.14 × 9 inches × 9 inches = 254.34 square inches. So the sector is $\frac{1}{6}$ × 254.34 = $\frac{254.34}{6}$ or 42.39 square inches.

TRY IT!

A game has a circular spinner that has a radius of 2 inches and is divided into sections. One of the sections has a central angle that measures 120°. What is the area of this section of the spinner? Use $\pi = 3.14$. Round your answer to nearest hundredths place.

EXAMPLE 3

Find the area of the shaded sector in the drawing below. Use 3.14 for π. Round your answer to the nearest hundredth.

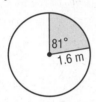

You can solve this problem by finding the area of a sector.

Use the formula $A = \dfrac{\text{central angle}}{360} \times \pi r^2$.

$$A = \frac{\text{central angle}}{360} \times \pi r^2$$

$\qquad = \dfrac{81}{360} \times \pi \times 1.6^2$ \qquad Substitute.

$\qquad = 0.225 \times 3.14 \times 1.6^2$ \qquad Express $\dfrac{81}{360}$ as a decimal. Use 3.14 for π.

$\qquad = 1.80864$ \qquad Multiply.

$\qquad \approx 1.81$ \qquad Round to the nearest hundredth.

So the area of the shaded sector is about 1.81 square meters.

▶ **Understanding the Solution** Is your answer reasonable? The central angle of 81° is a little less than 90°, so the sector is a bit less than one-fourth of the circle. The area of the whole circle is $A = \pi \times 1.6^2$ or about 8 square meters. $\frac{1}{4} \times 8 = 2$. So the area of the sector is less than 2. The answer of about 1.81 square meters seems reasonable.

TRY IT!

Laurie wants to plant flowers in the shaded section of the garden. What is the area of the shaded section of the garden? Use 3.14 for π. Round your answer to the nearest tenth.

Exercises

1 Tyler has a paper plate with a radius of 5 inches. He cuts out a sector of the plate. The sector has a central angle of 60°. What is the area of the sector that he cuts out? Leave your answer in terms of π.

Show your work.

Answer _____

MULTIPLE CHOICE

2 A sector of a circle with a central angle of 117° is part of a circle. Which fraction and decimal pair represents the part of the circle?

A $\frac{13}{40}$, 0.0307

B $\frac{13}{40}$, 0.325

C $\frac{13}{40}$, 0.0325

D $\frac{39}{90}$, 0.43

3 Which expression below would you use to find the area of a sector of a circle with a radius of 5 inches and a central angle of 54°?

A $\frac{6}{40} \times 3.14 \times 5$

B $\frac{1}{6} \times 3.14 \times 5 \times 2$

C $\frac{3}{20} \times 5 \times 5$

D $\frac{3}{20} \times 3.14 \times 5 \times 5$

4 Find the area of a sector of a circle whose central angle is 90° and whose radius is 6 feet. Leave answer in terms of π.

A 1.5π

B 3π

C 9π

D 24π

5 Find the area of the shaded sector in the circle below. Use 3.14 for π. Round your answer to the nearest hundredth.

A 37.68 square inches

B 6.28 square inches

C 452.16 square inches

D 376.8 square inches

6 A sector of a circle with a central angle of 42° is a fractional part of a circle. Which fraction below gives the correct fractional part?

A $\frac{7}{60}$

B $\frac{3}{20}$

C $\frac{21}{190}$

D $\frac{1}{9}$

7 Find the area of a sector of a circle whose
central angle measures 144º. The radius
is 3 feet. Leave your answer in terms of π.

A 2.4π square feet

B 3.6π square feet

C 4.2π square feet

D 7.2π square feet

EXTENDED RESPONSE

8 A circular rug has wedges of different colors. The drawing shows one of the wedges.

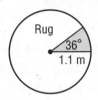

Part A

Find the area of the sector. Use 3.14 for π. Round your answer to nearest hundredth.

Show your work.

Answer _____

Part B

What happens to the area of the sector if the central angle is doubled?

Show your work.

Answer _____

LESSON 7.9   *Problem-Solving Strategy: Using Information in Figures*

New York Performance Indicators
6.PS.13 Model problems with picture/diagrams or physical objects
6.CN.5 Model situations with objects and representations and be able to draw conclusions

Understand the Strategy

Sometimes drawing a picture or using a physical model can help you simplify a problem. When you do this, be sure to read the problem carefully so the information you use in your drawing or model is correct.

Problem: Mark has a rectangular table whose top measures 5 feet by 3 feet. He decides to mark off 1-foot squares on the tabletop so he can paint them in alternating colors of yellow and blue. How many squares will he paint? Will it matter which color he starts with?

SOLUTION

What do you know?

Tabletop is a rectangle

Top measures 5 feet by 3 feet

Paint 1-foot yellow and blue squares on tabletop

What do you need to find?

Number of squares painted

Will the color he starts with matter?

Find the relationship.

To find the number of squares to be painted, make a model of the tabletop by drawing a 5-square by 3-square rectangle on 1-centimeter square graph paper.

He has 15 squares to paint.

To see if it matters which color he starts with, draw another rectangle like the first. On one rectangle, start by coloring the first square yellow and the next blue. Continue in same manner until all squares are colored. Do the same with the other rectangle, but start with blue. When finished count the number of each color of squares in each rectangle.

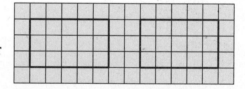

Yes, it matters which color he starts with. If he starts with yellow, he will have 8 yellow and 7 blue. If he starts with blue, he will have 8 blue and 7 yellow.

▶ **Understanding the Solution**   Mark will paint 15 squares on the top of the table. Since 15 is an odd number, he cannot have the same number of each color. He will have one more square of whatever color he starts with.

Exercises

1 Ms. Brown has two framed paintings that she wants to store in one box, one painting on top of the other. One framed painting is 10 inches long and 8 inches wide. The other painting is 12 inches long and 6 inches wide. What are the dimensions of the smallest box possible? How much area will the bottom of the box take up on a shelf?

Show your work.

Answer _____

_____

2 Lisa has a rectangular garden that is 6 feet long and 4 feet wide. She wants to plant a rose bush every 2 feet around the perimeter of the garden. If she starts in one corner, how many rose bushes will she have to plant?

Show your work.

Answer _____

MULTIPLE CHOICE

1 Triangle *ABC* is similar to triangle *DEF*. Which statement is always true?

   A The corresponding sides of △*ABC* are longer than the sides of △*DEF*.

   B The corresponding sides of △*ABC* are shorter than the sides of △*DEF*.

   C The corresponding sides of △*ABC* are equal in length to the sides of △*DEF*.

   D The corresponding angles of △*ABC* are equal in measure to the angles of △*DEF*.

2 What is the area of the trapezoid?

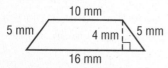

   A 22 square millimeters
   B 35 square millimeters
   C 52 square millimeters
   D 104 square millimeters

3 What is the area of the polygon?

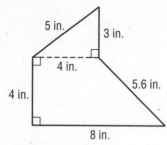

   A 29.6 square inches
   B 30 square inches
   C 47 square inches
   D 63 square inches

4 What is the volume of the rectangular prism?

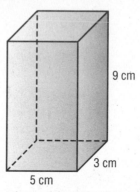

   A 24 cubic centimeters
   B 60 cubic centimeters
   C 135 cubic centimeters
   D 210 cubic centimeters

5 If the diameter of a circle is 104 meters, what is the measure of the radius?

   A 42 meters
   B 52 meters
   C 62 meters
   D 72 meters

6 What is the area of a circle with a radius of 9 millimeters?

   A 28.26 square millimeters
   B 56.52 square millimeters
   C 254.34 square millimeters
   D 1017.36 square millimeters

7 A circular disk has a radius of 7 inches and is divided into 3 sectors of different colors. The blue sector has a central angle of 120°; the red sector has a central angle of 168°. The remaining sector is yellow.

Part A

What is the area of the circular disk? Use 3.14 for π.

Show your work.

Answer _____

Part B

What is the area of the yellow sector of the disk? Use 3.14 for π. Round your answer to hundredths.

Show your work.

Answer _____

8 Use the prism to answer parts A and B.

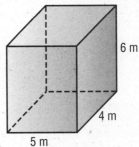

Part A

What is the volume of the prism?

Show your work.

Answer _____

Part B

Draw a different rectangular prism that has the same volume as the prism above.

Show your work.

Answer _____

LESSON 8.1 # Capacity and Volume of Rectangular Prisms

New York Performance Indicators

6.M.1   Measure capacity and volume of a rectangular prism
6.PS.11 Translate from a picture/diagram to a number or symbolic expression
6.CN.2 Explore and explain the relationship between mathematical ideas
6.R.8   Use mathematics to show and understand physical phenomena
         (i.e., determine the perimeter of a bulletin board)

VOCABULARY

The **capacity** of a container refers to the amount that the container can hold.

REVIEW

Understanding Volume of Rectangular Prisms

The volume, V, of a rectangular prism can be found in the following ways:

- Count the number of cubic units that fill the prism.

  unit cube

- Find the product of its length, ℓ, width, w, and height, h.

$$V = \ell wh$$

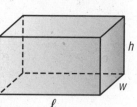

What You Should Know

The capacity of a container that is in the shape of a rectangular prism can be found by finding its volume in cubic units.

The volume measurement can be written using abbreviations and an exponent of 3.

Examples

Cubic units = units^3

Cubic inches = in^3

Cubic feet = ft^3

Cubic meters = m^3

Finding the Volume of Rectangular Prisms

To find the volume of a prism, you need to identify its three dimensions, *length, width,* and *height.* Be sure all three dimensions have the same unit of measure.

EXAMPLE 1

What is the volume of the rectangular prism?

You can solve this problem by counting the number of unit cubes.
Count the number of units in the top layer. Then multiply by the number of layers.

$$4 \text{ cubes} \times 2 \text{ layers} = 8 \text{ cubes}$$
$$\text{Volume} = 8 \text{ cubic units or } 8 \text{ units}^3$$

▶ **Understanding the Solution** The important thing is to make sure each layer of the prism has the same number of cubes. The volume of this figure is measured in cubic units since no other measures are given.

TRY IT!

What is the volume of the rectangular prism?

EXAMPLE 2

What is the volume, in cubic centimeters, of the rectangular prism?

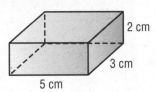

You can solve this problem by using the formula $V = \ell wh$ to find the volume of the prism.
Identify the *length*, *width*, and *height* of the prism.

length = 5 centimeters, width = 3 centimeters, height = 2 centimeters

Substitute 5 centimeters for ℓ, 3 centimeters for w, and 2 centimeters for h, then multiply.

$$V = 5 \text{ centimeters} \times 3 \text{ centimeters} \times 2 \text{ centimeters}$$
$$= 30 \text{ cubic centimeters}$$

▶ **Understanding the Solution** Because multiplication is commutative, it does not matter which measures you identify as the length, width, and height. If you had let the length equal 3 centimeters, the width equal 5 centimeters, and the height equal 2 centimeters, the volume would still equal 30 cubic centimeters.

What is the volume of the rectangular prism?

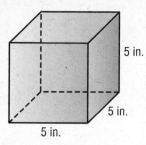

5 in.

5 in.

5 in.

Exercises

SHORT RESPONSE

1 Maria has a pencil box in the shape of the rectangular prism shown below.

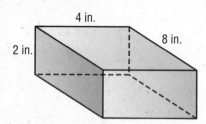

4 in.

8 in.

2 in.

What is the volume, in cubic inches, of Maria's pencil box?

Show your work.

Answer _____ cubic inches

2 What is the volume, in cubic inches, of the rectangular prism?

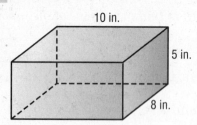

10 in.

5 in.

8 in.

Show your work.

Answer _____ cubic inches

3 The diagram below shows a rectangular prism that Kara built using blocks.

Key: = 1 cubic meter

What is the volume of the rectangular prism?

A 15 cubic meters
B 25 cubic meters
C 30 cubic meters
D 31 cubic meters

4 What is the volume of the rectangular solid shown below?

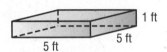

1 ft
5 ft
5 ft

A 11 cubic feet
B 25 cubic feet
C 26 cubic feet
D 30 cubic feet

5 Daniel put his rock collection in the shoebox shown below.

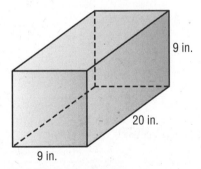

9 in.
20 in.
9 in.

What is the volume of the shoebox?

A 38 cubic inches
B 261 cubic inches
C 360 cubic inches
D 1,620 cubic inches

6 What is the volume of a rectangular prism having a length of 9 yards, a width of 5 yards, and a height of 6 yards?

A 20 cubic yards
B 45 cubic yards
C 99 cubic yards
D 270 cubic yards

7 The length of a rectangular prism is 5 centimeters and its width is 1 centimeter. If the height is 9 centimeters, what is the volume of the rectangular prism?

A 14 cubic centimeters
B 45 cubic centimeters
C 19 cubic centimeters
D 225 cubic centimeters

8 What is the volume of the rectangular solid shown below?

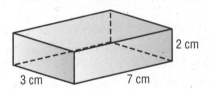

2 cm
3 cm
7 cm

A 12 cubic centimeters
B 17 cubic centimeters
C 40 cubic centimeters
D 42 cubic centimeters

9 Christopher's model of a rectangular prism that has a volume of 24 cubic centimeters is shown below.

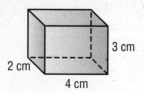

3 cm
2 cm
4 cm

Part A

Change the measures of the length and height of Christopher's model so that this new model will still have a volume of 24 cubic centimeters.

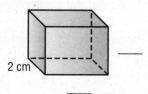

2 cm

Show your work.

Answer _____

Part B

How can you verify that your model still has a volume of 24 cubic centimeters?

Show your work.

Answer _____

Part C

Find the dimensions of another rectangular prism that has a volume of 24 cubic centimeters.

Show your work.

Answer _____

LESSON 8.2 Customary Units of Capacity

New York Performance Indicators

6.M.2 Identify customary units of capacity (cups, pints, quarts, and gallons)

6.M.3 Identify equivalent customary units of capacity (cups to pints, pints to quarts, and quarts to gallons)

6.PS.11 Translate from a picture/diagram to a number or symbolic expression

6.PS.21 Explain the methods and reasoning behind the problem solving strategies used

6.PS.22 Discuss whether a solution is reasonable in the context of the original problem

VOCABULARY

A **cup** (c) is a customary unit that is used to measure capacity.

1 **pint** (pt) = 2 cups

1 **quart** (qt) = 2 pints

1 **gallon** (gal) = 4 quarts

REVIEW

Understanding Customary Units of Capacity

A table can be used to change between units of measure.

Converting Units of Capacity		
Larger Unit	*Multiply*	**Smaller Unit**
pints	× 2	cups
quart	× 2	pints
gallon	× 4	quarts
Smaller Unit	*Divide*	**Larger Unit**
cups	÷ 2	pints
pints	÷ 2	quarts
quarts	÷ 4	gallons

What You Need to Know

Below are examples of familiar containers for these customary units of capacity. Having a picture in your mind of these containers is helpful when deciding which unit is larger or smaller than another.

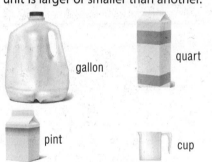

gallon

quart

pint

cup

Converting Customary Units of Capacity

When changing to a smaller unit, multiply. When changing to a larger unit, divide.

EXAMPLE 1

Amanda's pool holds 76 gallons of water. How many quarts of water is this?

You can use the conversion table to help you decide that you need to multiply to change from gallons to quarts. This is a change from a larger unit to a smaller unit.

Larger Unit	*Multiply*	Smaller Unit
gallon	× 4	quarts

You are changing from a larger unit to a smaller unit. Since 1 gallon equals 4 quarts, multiply by 4.

$$\text{gallons} \rightarrow \text{quarts}$$
$$76 \times 4 = 304$$

So, 76 gallons = 304 quarts.

▶ **Understanding the Solution**   Ask yourself if the solution makes sense. It makes sense that it will take many more quarts than gallons to fill the pool, since a quart holds less than a gallon. So, the answer does make sense.

TRY IT!

Complete: 12 pints = ▮▮▮ cups

| 1 pint = 2 cups |

EXAMPLE 2

A recipe for a fruit punch calls for 3 quarts of orange juice. How many pints of orange juice are needed?

You can use the conversion table to help you decide that you need to multiply to change from quarts to pints. This is a change from a larger unit to a smaller unit.

Larger Unit	Multiply	Smaller Unit
quarts	× 2	pints

Change from quarts to pints. Since 1 quart = 2 pints, multiply by 2.

$$\text{quarts} \rightarrow \text{pints}$$
$$3 \times 2 = 6$$

The recipe calls for 6 pints of orange juice.

▶ **Understanding the Solution**   Ask yourself if the solution makes sense. It makes sense that it will take more pints than the number of quarts of orange juice, since a pint is smaller than a quart. So, the answer does make sense.

TRY IT!

Tomas buys a 3-gallon tub of ice cream. How many pints of ice cream does Tomas buy?

| 1 gallon = 8 pints |

EXAMPLE 3

A store advertises a 12-pack of soymilk for $4.50. Each of the 12 containers is a pint. What is the equivalent capacity of the 12-pack in quarts?

You can use the conversion table to decide that you need to divide to change from pints to quarts. This is a change from a smaller unit to a larger unit.

Smaller Unit	*Divide*	Larger Unit
pints	÷ 2	quarts

Change from pints to quarts. Since 1 quart = 2 pints, divide by 2.

$$\text{pints} \rightarrow \text{quarts}$$
$$12 \div 2 = 6$$

The 12-pack of soymilk has an equivalent capacity of 6 quarts.

▶ **Understanding the Solution**   Ask yourself if the solution makes sense. It makes sense that it will take fewer quarts than pints to hold the soymilk, since a quart is larger than a pint. So, the answer does make sense.

TRY IT!

Janie has a container that holds 16 cups of lemonade. How many pints of lemonade does her container hold?

1 pint = 2 cups

Exercises

SHORT RESPONSE

1 Bernie poured 5 quarts of paint into a container. How many pints did he pour?

1 quart = 2 pints

Show your work.

Answer _____ pints

2 A carton holds 8 cups of milk. How many pints does it hold?

| 1 pint = 2 cups |

A 2
B 4
C 16
D 32

3 A crate of ice cream holds 24 quarts of rocky road ice cream. How many gallons of rocky road is this?

| 1 gallon = 4 quarts |

A 3
B 6
C 12
D 192

4 A nurse has a 6-pint bottle of water in her office. How many quarts of water does the nurse have?

| 1 quart = 2 pints |

A 1
B 3
C 12
D 24

5 Tina has a total of 4 pints of her favorite barbeque sauce in her pantry. If a recipe calls for 1 cup of barbeque sauce, how many times can she make that recipe?

| 1 pint = 2 cups |

A 8
B 16
C 32
D 64

6 On average, Becca drinks 2 quarts of water daily. How many cups of water does Becca drink daily?

| 1 quart = 4 cups |

A 1
B 4
C 8
D 16

7 Harold wants to mix up a can of frozen lemonade concentrate. The directions say that when mixed with $4\frac{1}{3}$ cans of water, it makes 2 quarts of lemonade. Which of the following pitchers cannot hold all of the lemonade?

| 1 gallon = 4 quarts |
| 1 quart = 2 pints |

A 4-pint pitcher
B 1-gallon pitcher
C $\frac{1}{2}$-gallon pitcher
D $3\frac{1}{2}$-pint pitcher

8 Alicia poured two large buckets of water into 1-gallon and 1-pint containers. Each large bucket contains 32 quarts of water.

| 1 gallon = 4 quarts |
| 1 quart = 2 pints |

Part A

How many 1-gallon containers did Alicia need for the first bucket of water?

Show your work.

Answer _____ 1-gallon containers

Part B

How many 1-pint containers did Alicia need for the other bucket of water?

Show your work.

Answer _____ 1-pint containers

LESSON 8.3 — Metric Units of Capacity

New York Performance Indicators

6.M.4 Identify metric units of capacity (liter and milliliter)

6.M.5 Identify equivalent metric units of capacity (milliliter to liter and liter to milliliter)

6.PS.11 Translate from a picture/diagram to a number or symbolic expression

6.PS.21 Explain the methods and reasoning behind the problem solving strategies used

6.PS.22 Discuss whether a solution is reasonable in the context of the original problem

VOCABULARY

The **milliliter** (mL) and the **liter** (L) are the most common metric units used for measuring capacity.

1 **liter** (L) = 1,000 milliliters

1 **milliliter** (mL) = 0.001 liter

REVIEW

Understanding Customary Units of Capacity

A table can be used to change between the most commonly used units of metric measure, the liter and the milliliter.

Converting Units of Capacity		
Larger Unit	*Multiply*	Smaller Unit
liters	× 1,000	milliliters
Smaller Unit	*Divide*	Larger Unit
milliliters	÷ 1,000	liters

What You Need to Know

Below are examples of familiar containers for both metric units of capacity. Having a picture in your mind of these containers is helpful when deciding which unit is larger or smaller than another.

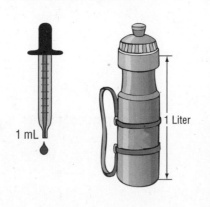

1 mL

1 Liter

Converting Metric Units of Capacity

You will need to either multiply or divide when changing from one metric unit of capacity to another.

EXAMPLE 1

George's water bottle holds 2 liters of water. How many milliliters of water is this?

You can use the conversion table to help you decide that you need to multiply to change from liters to milliliters. This is a change from a larger unit to a smaller unit.

Larger Unit	*Multiply*	Smaller Unit
liters	× 1,000	milliliters

When changing from a larger unit to a smaller unit, you multiply. Since 1 liter equals 1,000 milliliters, multiply by 1,000.

$$\text{liters} \rightarrow \text{milliliters}$$
$$2 \times 1,000 = 2,000$$

So, the water bottle holds 2,000 milliliters of water.

▶ **Understanding the Solution**   Ask yourself if the solution makes sense. It makes sense that it will take many more milliliters than liters to fill the water bottle, since a milliliter is a smaller amount than a liter. So, the answer does make sense.

TRY IT!

Complete: 5 liters = ▨▨▨ milliliters

1 liter = 1,000 milliliters

EXAMPLE 2

Mrs. Harrison buys a 5-liter box of evaporated milk. How many 250-milliliter servings can she get from that box of milk?

You can use the conversion table to help you decide that you need to multiply to change from liters to milliliters. This is a change from a larger unit to a smaller unit.

Larger Unit	*Multiply*	Smaller Unit
liters	× 1,000	milliliters

Change from liters to milliliters. Since 1 liter = 1,000 milliliters, multiply by 1,000.

$$\text{liters} \rightarrow \text{milliliters}$$
$$5 \times 1,000 = 5,000$$

Divide to find out how many 250-milliliter servings you can get out of 5,000 milliliters.

$$5,000 \div 250 = 20$$

A 5-liter box of evaporated milk contains twenty 250-milliliter servings.

▶ **Understanding the Solution**   Besides solving this problem in the two steps shown, you might have recognized that 4 × 250 milliliters is equal to 1,000 milliliters or 1 liter. This means that 4 × 5 = 20 servings.

TRY IT!

Mr. Boudinot buys a 3-liter bottle of water. How many 200-milliliter servings can he get from that bottle of water?

1 liter = 1,000 milliliters

EXAMPLE 3

In Ms. Shannon's science class, tadpoles are hatching in a container of 355 milliliters of water. How many liters of water are in the container?

You can use the conversion table to decide that you need to divide to change from milliliters to liters. This is a change from a smaller unit to a larger unit.

Smaller Unit	*Divide*	Larger Unit
milliliters	÷ 1,000	liters

Change from milliliters to liters. Since 1 liter = 1,000 milliliters, divide by 1,000.

$$\text{milliliters} \rightarrow \text{liters}$$
$$355 \div 1,000 = 0.355$$

There are 0.355 liters of water in the container.

▶ **Understanding the Solution**   Besides dividing by 1,000 to solve this problem, you might have recognized that you can also multiply by 0.001 when changing from milliliters to liters. For example: 355 × 0.001 = 0.355.

TRY IT!

Wil has a bottle that holds 750 milliliters of lemonade. How many liters of lemonade does his bottle hold?

1 liter = 1,000 milliliters

Exercises

1 A container holds 875 milliliters. How many liters does it hold?

Show your work.

Answer _____ liters

2 A carton holds 64 milliliters of milk. How many liters does it hold?

- **A** 0.064
- **B** 6.4
- **C** 640
- **D** 6,400

3 A carton holds 2 liters of heavy cream. How many milliliters of heavy cream is this?

- **A** 0.02
- **B** 0.002
- **C** 200
- **D** 2,000

4 Pam bought a bottle containing 250 milliliters of mouthwash. How many liters of mouthwash are in the bottle?

- **A** 25
- **B** 2.5
- **C** 0.25
- **D** 0.025

5 Jim brought 4.5 liters of fruit punch to a picnic. How many milliliters of fruit punch did he bring?

- **A** 45,000
- **B** 4,500
- **C** 450
- **D** 0.45

6 Laura put 4 milliliters of perfume in each of 8 vials. How many liters of perfume is this in all?

- **A** 32
- **B** 3.2
- **C** 0.32
- **D** 0.032

7 A recipe calls for 350 milliliters of milk. Frannie has exactly 0.5 liters of milk in her refrigerator. After she makes the recipe, how many liters of milk will she have left?

- **A** 0.15
- **B** 1.5
- **C** 349.5
- **D** 1.500

8 Darin buys laundry detergent at a local store.
He paid $5.49 for a 1.5-liter bottle of Wave.
He paid $7.69 for a 2,500-milliliters of Hurray.

Part A

How many milliliters of the Wave brand did Darin buy?

Show your work.

Answer _____ milliliters

Part B

How many liters of the Hurray brand did Darin buy?

Show your work.

Answer _____ liters

Problem-Solving Strategy: Modeling with Physical Objects

New York Performance Indicators

6.PS.13 Model problems with pictures/diagrams or physical objects

Understand the Strategy

You can use pictures/diagrams or physical objects to help you solve problems that involve positions.

Problem: Ben, Callie, David, and Elliot are waiting in line to buy their tickets to see a movie at the theater. Elliot is somewhere in front of David. Ben is somewhere in front of Elliot and somewhere behind Callie. What is the order of these four people?

SOLUTION

What do you know?

Elliot is somewhere in front of David.

Ben is somewhere in front of Elliot.

Ben is somewhere behind Callie.

What do you need to find?

The order of these four people

Find the relationship.

Use physical objects to model the relationship among these four people. Write the first letter of each person's name on a separate index card.

TRY IT!

Begin with the first item of what you know. Arrange your cards to show that Elliot is somewhere in front of David.

Ben is somewhere in front of Elliot. Add Ben's card to the model.

Ben is somewhere behind Callie. Add Callie's card to the model.

Callie is first in line to purchase a ticket. Behind her, is Ben, then Elliot, and finally David.

> ▶ **Understanding the Solution** Always return to the original problem and determine that the information given is correctly represented in the model you made. Elliot is before David. Ben is before Elliot. Ben is after Callie.

Exercises

SHORT RESPONSE

1 Evelyn is planning on reading five books this summer. She wants to read *Old Yeller* sometime before she reads *Abel's Island* but sometime after she reads *Tornado*. She plans to read *Cousins* before she reads *Abel's Island* but after *Old Yeller*. She plans to read *Tornado* after *Summer of the Swans*. In what order does Evelyn plan to read these five books?

Show your work.

Answer _____ _____ _____

   _____ _____

2 There are five children in the Romer family. Dan is 5 years older than Joe but 4 years younger than Flora. Betty is 4 years younger than Irene and 3 years older than Joe. Flora is older than Irene. Order the children from oldest to youngest.

Show your work.

Answer _____

LESSON 8.5 Measuring Capacity

New York Performance Indicators

6.M.6 Determine the tool and technique to measure with an appropriate level of precision: capacity

6.M.9 Determine personal references for capacity

6.CM.1 Provide an organized thought process that is correct, complete, coherent, and clear

VOCABULARY

The **precision** of a measurement depends on the unit of measure you use. The smaller the unit of measure you use, the greater the precision.

REVIEW

Understanding Measuring Capacity

There is no such thing as a truly exact measurement. Each measurement contains a degree of uncertainty due the limits of the measuring tools and the people using them.

The gallon container shown below shows divisions for quarts.

This container has a degree of precision of 1 quart.

What You Need to Know

When measuring capacity:

- Cups are more precise than pints.
- Pints are more precise than quarts.
- Quarts are more precise than gallons.
- Milliliters are more precise than liters.

Having a personal reference for each unit of capacity can help you when deciding which unit to use when measuring capacity.

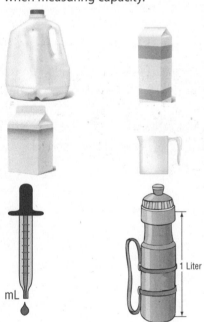

Measuring Capacity

When measuring capacity you first need to decide which is the best unit of capacity to use.

EXAMPLE 1

Which customary unit of measure of capacity would you find on the label of the real-life object represented? Write cup, pint, quart, or gallon.

Think of your own personal references for cups, pints, quarts, and gallons. The number provided on the label of the container is also helpful when deciding the unit of capacity.

Would it seem reasonable that the container holds 1 cup, 1 pint, 1 quart, or 1 gallon of milk?

There is 1 gallon of milk in the container.

Understanding the Solution   Ask yourself if the unit makes sense. It makes sense, since a large milk container is larger than 1 cup, 1 pint, and 1 quart.

TRY IT!

Which metric unit of measure of capacity would you find on the label of the real-life object represented? Write milliliters or liters.

Precision

When measuring capacity, you can only be as precise as the smallest unit on the measuring tool. The smaller the unit, the more precise the measurement is.

EXAMPLE 2

Which measurement is more precise, 28 liters or 28,054 milliliters?

Use your own personal reference to help you decide which unit is the smaller unit.
28,054 milliliters is the more precise measurement.

Understanding the Solution   The smaller unit is milliliters. So, measuring an amount of fluid in milliliters is more precise than measuring that same amount in liters.

TRY IT!

Which measurement is more precise, 6,425 milliliters or 7 liters?

EXAMPLE 3

Which measurement is more precise, 5 pints or 3 quarts?

Use your own personal reference to help you decide which unit is the smaller unit.
5 pints is the more precise measurement.

Understanding the Solution   The smaller unit is pints. So, measuring an amount of fluid in pints is more precise than measuring that same amount in quarts.

TRY IT!

Which measurement is more precise, 8 pints or 15 cups?

Exercises

SHORT RESPONSE

1 Harold wants to know how much water is in his backyard swimming pool so that he can figure out the right amount of chemicals to put in it. His owner's manual has been damaged by water, so the only information he has on the amount of water his pool holds is the number 18,000. He needs to know the units. Which is the most likely unit: cups, pints, quarts, or gallons?

Explain your answer.

Answer_____

_____

MULTIPLE CHOICE

2 Bertie wants to measure the amount of water in her fish tank. What unit of measure should she use?

A kilometers
B liters
C milliliters
D meters

3 George takes the thermos shown below, full of hot chocolate, to work. Which customary unit of measure of capacity would you find on the label? Hint: the cap holds 1 cup of fluid.

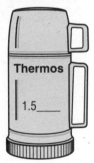

A quarts
B cups
C pints
D gallons

4 Michael has gerbils. He hangs a water bottle on the side of his gerbils' cage. Which unit of measure of capacity would you find on the label?

A milliliters
B gallons
C cups
D liters

5 Which measurement is more precise?

A 24 cups
B 11 pints
C 5.5 quarts
D 1.5 gallons

6 Which measurement is more precise?

    A 129 gallons

    B 17 quarts

    C 100 pints

    D 4 cups

7 Which is a true statement?

    A 8,100 milliliters is not a more precise measurement than 80 liters.

    B 2,351 milliliters is a more precise measurement than 23 liters.

    C 7.5 liters is a more precise measurement than 7,511 milliliters.

    D 24 liters is a more precise measurement than 23 liters.

EXTENDED RESPONSE

8 Julie wants to determine the capacity of her glass mixing bowl.

Part A

In order to make the most precise measurement, should she measure the amount of liquid it holds in cups, pints, quarts, or gallons? Explain.

Explain your answer.

Answer _____

_____

Part B

When Julie rotated the bowl she noticed it has a 1-liter mark on it. Could she use this bowl to get a measure of the amount of liquid in a 1-serving can of vegetable soup? Explain.

Explain your answer.

Answer _____

_____

LESSON 8.6 Estimating Volume, Area, and Circumference

New York Performance Indicators

6.M.7 Estimate volume, area, and circumference (see figures identified in geometry strand)

6.M.8 Justify the reasonableness of estimates

6.R.7 Use mathematics to show and understand physical phenomena (i.e., determine the perimeter of a bulletin board)

VOCABULARY

An **estimate** is a number close to an exact value. An estimate indicates *about* how much.

REVIEW

Understanding How to Estimate Volume, Area, and Circumference

The symbol $\approx$ means *approximately* or *about*.

Here are some estimation strategies:

Rounding: Use place value to round numbers to ones that make calculations easier.

Example: $43 \times 59 \approx 40 \times 60 = 2,400$

With Fractions: Use a basic fact that is easy to divide by the denominator of the fraction.

Example: $\frac{1}{2}(5.9) \approx 6 \div 2 = 3$

Range of Values: Find the upper bound by rounding up and multiplying. Find the lower bound by rounding down and multiplying.

Example: 43×59

rounds up to $50 \times 60 = 3,000$

rounds down to $40 \times 50 = 2,000$

The exact product is between 2,000 and 3,000.

What you should know

You should be familiar with these formulas.

area of a triangle
$A = \frac{1}{2}bh$

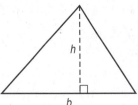

area of a square
$A = s^2$

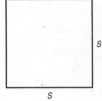

area of a rectangle
$A = \ell w$

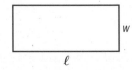

area of a rhombus
$A = bh$

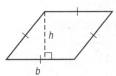

area of a trapezoid
$A = \frac{1}{2}h(b_1 + b_2)$

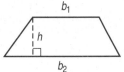

volume of a rectangular prism:
$V = \ell w h$

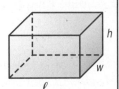

area and circumference of a circle:
$A = \pi r^2$
$C = \pi d$ or $C = 2\pi r$

Estimating Volume, Area, and Circumference

You can estimate the volume, area, and circumference of a figure by using the appropriate formula and an estimation strategy.

EXAMPLE 1

Estimate the volume of a rectangular prism that is 9.8 centimeters long, 7.2 centimeters wide, and 4.6 centimeters high.

You can solve this problem by using the formula for the volume, $V = \ell wh$, and rounding. Round each dimension to the nearest whole number. Then substitute the values into the formula.

> *Length:* 9.8 centimeters rounds to 10 centimeters
> *Width:* 7.2 centimeters rounds to 7 centimeters
> *Height:* 4.6 centimeters round to 5 centimeters
> $V = \ell wh \approx 10 \times 7 \times 5$ or about 350

So the volume of the prism is about 350 cubic centimeters.

▶ **Understanding the Solution**   The estimated volume is an amount that is close to the exact answer.

TRY IT!

Estimate the volume of the rectangular prism with a length of 3.2 meters, a width of 4.9 meters, and a height of 2.3 meters.

EXAMPLE 2

A triangle has a 26-foot base and a 12-foot height. About how many square feet is the area of this triangle?

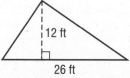

You can solve this problem by using the formula $A = \frac{1}{2}bh$ and a basic fact that is easy to divide by the denominator of the fraction.
Estimate the product of the base × height. Find factors that are easy to multiply and easily divided by 2.

Base: 26 feet rounds to 30 feet
Height: 12 feet rounds to 10 feet
Base × height $\approx 30 \times 10$ or 300 square feet.

Divide 300 by 2 to find $\frac{1}{2}bh \approx 300 \div 2 \approx 150$

The triangle has an area of about 150 square feet.

▶ **Understanding the Solution**   There are many ways to estimate a product. It is best to find numbers that makes the calculations easier than the original problem, while at the same time keeping the estimate reasonable. The closer the numbers are rounded to their actual values, the more reasonable the estimate will be.

A trapezoid has a 14-inch base and a 9.5-inch base. Its height is 3.8 inches. About how many square inches is the area of this trapezoid?

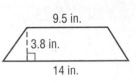

9.5 in.

3.8 in.

14 in.

EXAMPLE 3

A circle has a diameter of 8.5 centimeters. Between what estimated values would you find the exact circumference of the circle?

8.5 cm

You can solve this problem by using the formula $C = \pi d$. You will need to find the upper bound and lower bound for the range of values. You also need to know that the exact value for π (pi) is 3.1415926….

Find the upper bound value. Round 8.5 up to 9. Round the value of π to 4.

$$C = \pi d$$
$$C \approx 4(9) \text{ or } 36$$

Find the lower bound value. Round 8.5 down to 8. Round the value of π to 3.

$$C = \pi d$$
$$C \approx 3(8) \text{ or } 24$$

The circumference is between 24 and 36 centimeters.

▶ **Understanding the Solution**   There is no way to find the exact value for π since it is an irrational number. Therefore, all calculations for the circumference of a circle are estimates. Often, when solving problems for circumference, you will be asked to round the answer to a particular place value, such as the nearest tenth. When estimating, however, you want to round the numbers before calculating the circumference.

TRY IT!

A circle has a radius of 3.25 feet. Between what estimated values would you find the exact circumference of the circle?

3.25 ft

Exercises

1 A community garden is in the shape of a rectangle. It has a 235-foot width and a 578-foot length.

235 ft

578 ft

About how many square feet is the garden?

Show your work.

Answer about _____ square feet

MULTIPLE CHOICE

2 The diameter of a circle is 6 meters.

6 m

About how many meters is the circumference of the circle?

A 18   **B** 28

C 30   **D** 36

3 Marsha wants to paint a sign on a poster board with the shape of a trapezoid. The dimensions are shown below.

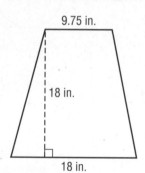

9.75 in.

18 in.

18 in.

About how many square inches is the area of the poster board?

A 50   **B** 100

C 150   **D** 300

4 Bryan drew a turtle on the paper shown below. About how many square inches is the area of the paper?

8.5 in.

8.5 in.

A 18 square inches

B 81 square inches

C 120 square inches

D 144 square inches

5 Which of the following is not a reasonable estimate for the area of a triangle whose base is 17 centimeters and whose height is 46 centimeters?

A 500 square centimeters

B 400 square centimeters

C 375 square centimeters

D 150 square centimeters

6 A rhombus with a 29-inch height and an 11-inch base is being cut out of a piece of plywood. Which is the best estimate for the area of the rhombus?

   A 150 square inches

   B 200 square inches

   C 250 square inches

   D 300 square inches

7 A circular window has been installed in an office building.

Which range of values best describes the circumference of the window?

   A between 3 and 8 meters

   B between 3 and 16 meters

   C between 2 and 4 meters

   D between 1.8 and 2 meters

EXTENDED RESPONSE

8 Wally drew a rectangle in the sand. The length of the rectangle is 36 inches and the width is 18 inches. He estimates the area of the rectangle to be 280 square inches.

Part A

Is this a reasonable estimate? Explain.

Show your work.

Answer _____

_____

_____

_____

Part B

Wally decides to dig out the sand in his rectangle, to a depth of 11 inches. Approximately how many cubic inches of sand will he remove?

Show your work.

Answer about _____ cubic inches

LESSON 8.7 Problem-Solving Strategy: Trial and Error

New York Performance Indicators
6.PS.12 Use trial and error and the process of elimination to solve problems

Understand the Strategy

You can use the "trial and error" strategy to help you solve problems when the trial answers are easy to check. This strategy can be thought of as try, check, and revise.

Problem: The height of a rectangular prism is 9 centimeters more than the width. The length is 5 centimeters and the volume is 50 cubic centimeters. What are the dimensions of the prism?

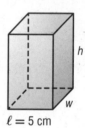

$\ell = 5$ cm

SOLUTION

What do you know?

Height = 9 centimeters more than the width

Length = 5 centimeters

Volume = 50 cubic centimeters

What do you need to find?

The measure of the height and width

Find the relationship.

Since you know the shape is a rectangular prism and you know the volume, you can use the formula for volume, $V = \ell wh$, and trial and error to help you solve this problem.

TRY IT!

Substitute the given values into the formula for volume:

$V = 50, \ell = 5$

$V = \ell \times w \times h$
$50 = 5 \times \underline{w \times h}$

Make an educated guess.   You know that $50 = 5 \times \underline{10}$.

So, now you know that $w \times h$ has to equal 10.

Try: 2×5

Check: The product, $50 = 5 \times 2 \times 5$, checks, but the height needs to be 9 more than the width. If the height equals 5 centimeters and the width equals 2 centimeters, then $5 - 2 = 3$, so a height of 5 and a width of 2 do not check.

Think: I need to try another set of factors.

Try: 1×10

Check: The product, $50 = 5 \times 1 \times 10$, checks, and the height is 9 more than the width since $10 - 1 = 9$. So, the answer of a height of 10 and a width of 1 checks.

The rectangular prism has a length of 5 centimeters, a height of 10 centimeters, and a width of 1 centimeter.

▶ **Understanding the Solution**   Always return to the original problem and determine that the numbers you select work for the information given. $50 = 5 \times 1 \times 10$ and $10 - 1 = 9$.

Exercises

SHORT RESPONSE

1 One weekend Nancy worked a total of 16 hours helping her dad paint his fence. She worked 2 hours more on Saturday than she worked on Sunday. How many hours did she work each day?

Show your work.

Answer _____ hours on Saturday _____ hours on Sunday

2 The length of a rectangular prism is 2 feet more than the width. The height is 6 feet and the volume is 48 cubic feet. What are the dimensions of the prism?

Show your work.

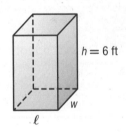

$h = 6$ ft

w

ℓ

Answer   length = _____ feet

width = _____ feet

height = _____ feet

MULTIPLE CHOICE

1 A label on a water bottle used for camping says that the bottle holds 3 pints of liquid. How many cups does it hold?

| 1 pint = 2 cups |

A 1.5 cups
B 6 cups
C 8 cups
D 12 cups

2 Hannah has a total of 2 gallons of her favorite lemonade in her refrigerator. If she drinks 1 quart of it each day, how many days will it take for her to drink all of her favorite lemonade?

| 1 gallon = 4 quarts |

A 24
B 16
C 8
D 6

3 Donald bought a bottle containing 750 milliliters of yogurt. How many liters of yogurt did he buy?

| 1 liter = 1,000 milliliters |

A 75
B 7.5
C 0.75
D 0.075

4 Eve wrote five emails. She wrote an email to Ann sometime before she wrote one to Bill but sometime after she wrote one to Cathy. She wrote Cathy after she wrote Dave. She wrote Fred before she wrote Bill but after she wrote Ann. Which list shows the order Eve wrote the five emails from first to last?

A Dave, Cathy, Ann, Fred, Bill
B Cathy, Dave, Ann, Fred, Bill
C Ann, Fred, Bill, Dave, Cathy
D Cathy, Ann, Dave, Fred, Bill

5 Which measurement is more precise?

A 3 gallons
B 48 cups
C 23 pints
D 13 quarts

6 The diameter of a circle is 11 meters.

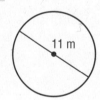

11 m

About how many meters is the circumference of the circle?

A 11
B 20
C 30
D 75

7 Cabrini's model of a rectangular prism that has a volume of 36 cubic centimeters is shown below.

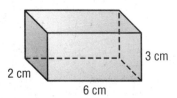

Part A

Change the measures of the length and height of Cabrini's model so that this new model will still have a volume of 36 cubic centimeters.

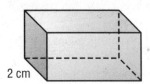

How can you verify that your model still has a volume of 36 cubic centimeters?

Show your work.

Answer _____

Part B

Find the dimensions of another rectangular prism that has a volume of 36 cubic centimeters.

Show your work.

Answer _____

LESSON 9.1 — Determining Mean, Mode, Median, and Range

New York Performance Indicators

6.S.5 Determine the mean, mode, and median for a given set of data
6.S.6 Determine the range for a given set of data
6.PS.5 Formulate problems and solutions from everyday situations

VOCABULARY

The **mean** of a set of data is the quotient found by adding the numbers in the set of data and dividing this sum by the number of addends.

The **mode** of a set of data is the number(s) or item(s) that occur most often. A set can have more than one mode.

The **median** is the middle number in a set of data when it is arranged in numerical order. If the data set has an even number, the median is the mean of the two middle numbers.

The **range** of a set of data is the difference between the greatest number and the least number in a set of data.

REVIEW

Understanding Mean, Mode, Median, and Range

Data can be described using measures of central tendency. The mean, mode, and median are three measures of central tendency.

- To find the mean of a set of data, you calculate the sum of the numbers in the set and then divide the sum by the number of addends in the set.

- To find the mode of a set of data, you find the number(s) that occur most often.

- To find the median of a set of data, you write the numbers in order from least to greatest (or greatest to least) and find the middle number. If there is an even number of data items, then you find the mean of the two middle numbers.

- To find the range of a set of data, you subtract the least number from the greatest number.

Applying Mean, Mode, Median, and Range

The number of students in Howard's math class each day last week is recorded in the table below. Describe the data using mean, median, mode, and range.

Day of the Week	Number of Students Present
Monday	20
Tuesday	22
Wednesday	23
Thursday	25
Friday	20

mean: $\dfrac{20 + 22 + 23 + 25 + 20}{5} = \dfrac{110}{5}$
$\qquad\qquad\qquad\qquad = 22$

median: 20, 20, <u>22</u>, 23, 25
  22 is the middle number

mode: <u>20</u>, 22, 23, 25, <u>20</u>
  20 is the number that occurs most often

range: $25 - 20 = 5$

Mean, Median, and Mode

Mean, median, and mode are all measures of central tendency. They are three of the ways of describing data.

The data set shows Dan's scores on his first six homework papers. Find the mean, median, and mode of the scores.

Test scores: 89, 77, 95, 91, 81, 95

You can solve this problem by following the steps shown in the instruction on the previous page.

mean: $\dfrac{89 + 77 + 95 + 91 + 81 + 95}{6} = \dfrac{528}{6}$

$= 88$

median: Order the data from least to greatest.

77, 81, <u>89</u>, <u>91</u>, 95, 95

Since there is an even number of scores, you must find the mean of the two middle numbers: $\dfrac{89 + 91}{2} = 90$.

mode: 89, 77, <u>95</u>, 91, 81, <u>95</u>

95 occurs most often.

▷ **Understanding the Solution** The mean of the data is 88, the median is 90, and the mode is 95. Note that each measure is different.

Last week Martha practiced her clarinet every day.

Minutes practicing: 30, 45, 22, 38, 30

Find the mean, median, and mode of the set of data.

Range

The range of a set of data is the difference between the greatest number and the least number.

Find the range of the set of data.
Height (in inches) of boys on the basketball team: 72, 73, 65, 67, 69, 72, 70

You can solve this problem by subtracting the least number from the greatest number.
The shortest person is 65 inches and the tallest person is 73 inches.

Range: $73 - 65 = 8$

▷ **Understanding the Solution** The range indicates how spread out the data set is. The range is 8 inches. It is not a large range in comparison to the data numbers, so this means that the data are fairly close in value.

Find the range of the set of data.

Age of teachers: 22, 53, 47, 60, 31, 34, 45

Exercises

1 Describe how to find the range of a set of data.

Show your work.

Answer _____

MULTIPLE CHOICE

2 What is the mean of the following data set?

9, 7, 14, 11, 14, 15, 14

A 12
B 13
C 14
D 15

3 What is the median of the following data set?

9, 7, 14, 11, 14, 15, 14

A 7
B 9
C 11
D 14

4 What are the modes of the following data set?

9, 7, 14, 11, 11, 15, 14

A 7 and 9
B 9 and 11
C 11 and 14
D 11, 14, and 15

5 What is the range of the following data set?

9, 7, 14, 11, 14, 15, 14

A 6
B 7
C 8
D 15

6 Twelve students were surveyed about their pets. Below is the number of pets each student reported that he or she owned.

2, 1, 4, 6, 3, 1, 5, 2, 3, 5, 2, 2

What is the mean of the data?

A 1
B 2
C 3
D 5

7 Tonia kept a record of how much money she made each time she babysat. Below is her record for the past 6 payments.

$45, $35, $50, $60, $75, $20

What is the median of this set of data?

A $45.00
B $47.50
C $50.00
D $55.00

8 Write down the names of seven of your classmates. Count the number of letters in each of their names and record the data.

Part A

What is the mean of the data?

Show your work.

Answer _____

Part B

What is the median of the data?

Show your work.

Answer _____

LESSON 9.2 Interpreting Graphs and Making Predictions

New York Performance Indicators

6.S.7 Read and interpret graphs

6.S.8 Justify predictions made from data

6.PS.14 Analyze problems by observing patterns

6.PS.17 Determine what information is needed to solve a problem

VOCABULARY

A **line graph** is a graph that uses points connected by line segments to represent changes in data over time.

A **pictograph** is a graph that compares data by using picture symbols.

A **bar graph** is a graph that compares data by using bars of different lengths or heights to show values.

REVIEW

Understanding Graphs and How to Use Them to Make Predictions

Graphs are visual ways to show data.

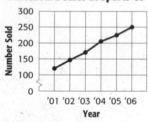

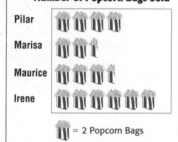

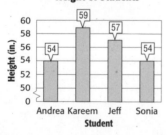

What You Should Know About Interpreting Graphs and Making Predictions

- Line graphs use points and lines to show how a set of data changes over time.

- Pictographs use pictures to compare data.

- Bar graph use bars to compare data.

Read and Interpret Graphs

Graphs provide ways to display data visually.

EXAMPLE 1

Use the line graph to answer the questions.

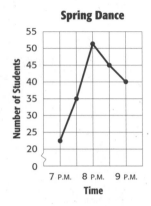

Spring Dance

a. **How many students were at the dance at 7:00 P.M.?**

b. **Predict how many students will still be at the dance at 9:30 P.M.**

You can solve this problem by reading and interpreting the line graph.

a. Look across the bottom of the graph and find the time of 7 P.M. Look up until you reach the point. From that point, look to the left. There were about 23 students at the dance at that time.

b. Extend the line graph in the direction it is going. If the trend continues, there will be about 35 students at the dance at 9:30 P.M.

▶ **Understanding the Solution**   Line graphs can be used to answer questions and make predictions about a set of data.

TRY IT!

Use the line graph to answer the questions.

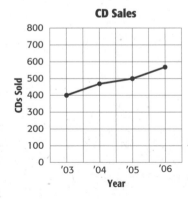

CD Sales

a. **How many CDs were sold in 2005?**

b. **Predict how many CDs will be sold in 2007.**

EXAMPLE 2

Use the pictograph to answer the questions.

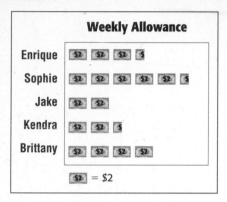

a. How much is Sophie's allowance each week?

b. Who gets the least amount of money each week for allowance?

You can solve this problem by reading and interpreting the pictograph.

a. Each picture represents $2, so count the number of pictures Sophie has next to her name. She has $5\frac{1}{2}$ pictures. Multiply that by 2, and she gets $11 each week.

b. Look at the graph to see who has the fewest pictures next to his or her name. Jake gets the least amount of money each week.

Understanding the Solution Pictographs can be used to answers questions about a set of data. The solution depends on the value assigned to each picture in the key of the graph.

TRY IT!

Use the pictograph to answer the questions.

a. How many siblings does Juan have?

b. How many more siblings does Patrick have than Maggie?

EXAMPLE 3

Use the bar graph to answer the questions.

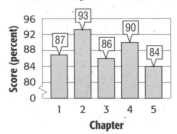

Pablo's Chapter Test Scores

a. What was Pablo's highest test score?

b. On what chapter test did Pablo score the lowest?

You can solve this problem by reading and interpreting the data in the bar graph.

a. The tallest bar represents the highest test score. He scored a 93 on the Chapter 2 test. 93 is his highest score.

b. The shortest bar represents his lowest score. He scored an 84 on the Chapter 5 Test. This was his lowest score.

▶ **Understanding the Solution** Bar graphs can be used to answers questions about a set of data.

TRY IT!

Use the bar graph to answer the questions.

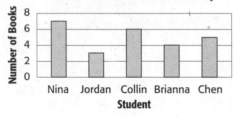

Books Checked Out of Library

a. Who checked out the most books at the library?

b. How many books did Brianna check out?

Exercises

SHORT RESPONSE

1 Manny wants to graph data showing the changes in temperature over a period of three months. Which type of graph should he use to display his data? Why?

Show your work.

Answer _____

MULTIPLE CHOICE

Use the graph below to answer questions 2–3.

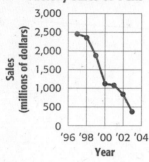

Factory Sales of VCRs

2 Which number best predicts the amount of factory sales in 2004?

A $50 million

B $500 million

C $700 million

D $1,100 million

3 What year showed the factory sales to be about $1,900 million?

A 1997

B 1998

C 1999

D 2000

Use the graph below to answer questions 4–5.

Number of Books Read

Rebecca

Lucita

Jerome

Mark

Kin

Peter

Keisha

Key: = 1 book

4 Who read exactly 4 books?

A Kin

B Mark

C Lucita

D Rebecca

5 Who read three fewer books than Keisha?

A Jerome

B Mark

C Peter

D Rebecca

Use the graph below to answer questions 6–7.

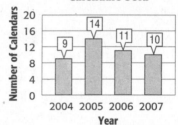

Calendars Sold

6 In what year were the fewest calendars sold?

A 2004

B 2005

C 2006

D 2007

7 What is the mean number of calendars sold each year from 2004 to 2007?

A 9

B 10

C 11

D 14

8 Use the graph below to answer parts A and B.

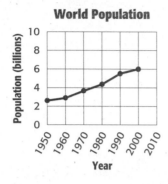

World Population

Part A

Use the data in the graph to describe the pattern or trend of the world population.

Show your work.

Answer _____

Part B

What do you predict the population to be in 2010?

Show your work.

Answer _____

LESSON 9.3 *Problem-Solving Strategy:* Choosing a Strategy

New York Performance Indicators

6.PS.8 Select an appropriate representation of a problem
6.PS.18 Determine the efficiency of different representations of a problem
6.PS.19 Differentiate between valid and invalid approaches

Understand the Strategy

When solving problems, it is important that you are able to choose which strategy is best to solve each problem. Below is a list of several strategies:

Draw a Picture	Draw a Diagram
Make a Table	Model with Physical Objects
Find a Pattern	Make an Organized List
Trial and Error	Use Information in Figures

Problem: At lunch, Alicia wants to sit with her two friends, Bob and Cathy. How many different ways can the three friends sit along one side of a rectangular cafeteria table?

SOLUTION

What do you know?

There are 3 friends in all.

They are going to sit in a row.

What do you need to find?

How many ways can they sit at the table?

Find the relationship.

You must first choose the strategy that would work best to solve this problem. Drawing a diagram may be the most efficient way. Draw a tree diagram to show all the ways they can sit at the table.

▶ **Understanding the Solution**   There are 6 different ways the students could be arranged at the table. You might also have chosen to model the problem using index cards to help you solve.

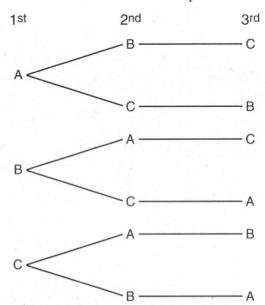

Exercises

1 In 2007, Bill earned $25,500, and Beth earned $30,000. Each year Bill will get a $1,000 raise, and Beth will get a $500 raise. In what year will Bill and Beth receive the same yearly pay? Which method did you use to solve this problem?

Show your work.

Answer _____

2 Mrs. Winn made an apple pie. Sarah asked for $\frac{3}{8}$ of it. Her brother wanted $\frac{1}{3}$ of it. Who asked for the biggest piece? Choose a strategy and solve the problem.

Show your work.

Answer _____

MULTIPLE CHOICE

1 What is the mean of the following data set?

42, 18, 32, 80, 20, 22, 28, 26, 20

A 20
B 32
C 62
D 288

2 What is the median of the following data set?

42, 18, 32, 80, 20, 22, 28, 26, 20

A 20
B 26
C 32
D 62

3 What is the mode of the following data set?

42, 18, 32, 80, 20, 22, 28, 26, 20

A 20
B 26
C 32
D 62

4 What is the range of the following data set?

42, 18, 32, 80, 20, 22, 28, 26, 20

A 18
B 32
C 62
D 80

Use the graph below to answer questions 5–6.

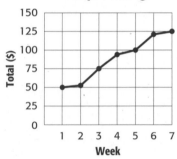

Kenya's Savings

5 At the end of Week 5, how much was Kenya's total savings?

A $50
B $75
C $100
D $125

6 Which statement is true?

A Kenya's total savings decreased from week 1 to week 2.
B Kenya saved more from week 4 to week 5 than any other week.
C Kenya increased her savings by the same amount each week.
D Kenya increased her saving about $25 from week 2 to week 3.

7 Use the graph below to answer parts A and B.

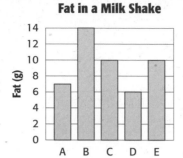

Fat in a Milk Shake

PART A

Which restaurant's milkshake contains 3 less grams of fat than restaurant C's milkshake?
Show your work.

Answer _____

PART B

Which restaurant's milkshake contains twice as much fat as restaurant A's milkshake?
Show your work.

Answer _____

8 Tom, Nathan, and Will each ordered a large pizza. Tom ate $\frac{5}{7}$ of his pizza, Nathan ate $\frac{7}{9}$ of his, and Will ate $\frac{3}{4}$ of his. Who ate the most pizza?

PART A

What strategy would you use to solve the problem?
Show your work.

Answer _____

PART B

Solve the problem.
Show your work.

Answer _____

PART 1

1 A store has 24-ounce bags of dog food on sale. You can buy 6 bags for $12 during the sale. Which proportion can be used to find the number of bags of dog food that can be bought for $20?

A $\frac{6}{12} = \frac{d}{20}$

B $\frac{6}{d} = \frac{20}{12}$

C $\frac{6}{20} = \frac{d}{24}$

D $\frac{6}{10} = \frac{20}{d}$

2 Nine students were surveyed about the number of siblings they have. Below is the number of siblings each student reported.

3, 1, 1, 2, 4, 2, 1, 1, 3

What is the mean of the data?

A 1

B 2

C 3

D 5

3 Jupiter has a surface area of 60,000,000,000 + 2,000,000,000 + 100,000,000 + 70,000,000 + 9,000,000 + 600,000 square kilometers. Which correctly gives this number in word form?

A sixty-two million, one hundred seventy-nine

B sixty-two billion, seventy-nine million, sixty thousand

C sixty-two billion, one hundred seventy-nine million, six hundred thousand

D sixth-two, one hundred seventy-nine, six thousand

4 Janine is cutting trapezoids out of a piece of construction paper to make a pattern. The trapezoid she is cutting is 6 inches high. It has a base of 3 inches and a base of 5 inches. Which is the area of the trapezoid?

A 15 square inches

B 20 square inches

C 24 square inches

D 30 square inches

5 What is the range of the following data set?

$$5, 12, 9, 11, 11, 15, 7$$

A 6

B 8

C 10

D 15

6 Find the area of a sector of a circle whose central angle measures 45°. The radius is 6 feet. Leave your answer in terms of π.

A 1.5π square feet

B 3.6π square feet

C 4.5π square feet

D 7.2π square feet

7 Fiona has $252 in her savings account. Her mother allows her to spend 21% on CDs. Approximately how much will Fiona be able to spend on CDs?

A $20

B $25

C $50

D $100

8 A recipe calls for $1\frac{1}{8}$ cups of blueberries for each batch of muffins. How many cups of blueberries do you need if you make $3\frac{5}{6}$ batches?

A $2\frac{1}{4}$

B $2\frac{2}{3}$

C $4\frac{5}{16}$

D $4\frac{2}{3}$

9 In a survey of students, $\frac{7}{18}$ said their favorite sport was tennis and $\frac{2}{3}$ said their favorite sport was soccer. How much greater is the fraction of students whose favorite sport is soccer?

A $\frac{5}{18}$

B $\frac{5}{54}$

C $\frac{2}{9}$

D $\frac{1}{3}$

10 Solve the following proportion. $\frac{7}{13} = \frac{y}{26}$

A 10

B 12

C 14

D 17

11 Simplify the expression $55 \div 11 + 6 \times (2 + 15)$.

A 32

B 64

C 107

D 187

12 Which is a good estimate for the circumference of a circle with a radius of 12 meters?

　A 3.5 meters

　B 6 meters

　C 36 meters

　D 72 meters

13 Which measurement is more precise?

　A 3.5 cups

　B 6 pints

　C 15 quarts

　D 2 gallons

14 Which of the following is the same as 71%?

　A $\frac{71}{10}$

　B $\frac{7}{10}$

　C $\frac{71}{100}$

　D $\frac{36}{50}$

15 What is the volume of a rectangular prism having a length of 7 yards, width of 3 yards, and a height of 5 yards?

　A 15 cubic yards

　B 38 cubic yards

　C 76 cubic yards

　D 105 cubic yards

16 Which proportion could you use to find the missing measure *x* if the two triangles are similar?

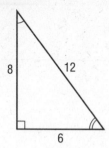

A $\frac{6}{12} = \frac{x}{6}$

B $\frac{1}{2} = \frac{x}{8}$

C $\frac{6}{x} = \frac{8}{12}$

D $\frac{x}{8} = \frac{12}{6}$

17 Which correctly gives fifty-four billion, three hundred twenty-nine million, three thousand, seven in expanded form?

A $50{,}000{,}000{,}000 + 4{,}000{,}000{,}000 + 300{,}000{,}000 + 20{,}000{,}000 + 9{,}000{,}000 + 3{,}000 + 7$

B $50{,}000{,}000 + 4{,}000{,}000 + 20{,}000 + 9{,}000 + 300 + 7$

C $50{,}000{,}000{,}000 + 4{,}000{,}000 + 200{,}000 + 90{,}000 + 3{,}000 + 7$

D $50{,}000{,}000 + 4{,}000{,}000{,}000 + 300{,}000 + 20{,}000 + 9{,}000 + 300 + 7$

18 Frank and Lauren are walking in a relay race. Frank walks at a rate of 3 miles per hour for 3.5 hours. Lauren walks at a rate of 4.5 miles per hour for 2 hours. Who walks farther? How much farther? Use the distance formula $d = r \times t$ to help you find the answer.

A Lauren, 0.5 miles farther

B Lauren, 1.5 miles farther

C Frank, 0.5 miles farther

D Frank, 1.5 miles farther

19 The volume of a rectangular prism is 84 cubic meters. The length of the prism is 7 meters and the width is 3 meters. What is the height of the prism?

A 1 meter

B 2 meters

C 3 meters

D 4 meters

20 What value for *n* makes the equation true?

$$n \times 7 = 1$$

A −7

B $\frac{1}{7}$

C $\frac{7}{8}$

D 1

21 Xavier put his fish in the aquarium shown below.

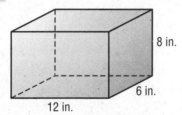

8 in.

6 in.

12 in.

What is the volume of the aquarium?

A 26 cubic inches

B 60 cubic inches

C 576 cubic inches

D 1,152 cubic inches

22 27 is 75% of what number?

    A 28

    B 30

    C 36

    D 40

23 Jane has 12 cups of yogurt. She has a parfait recipe that calls for 1 quart of yogurt. How many parfaits can Jane make?

    A 1

    B 3

    C 6

    D 12

24 Which expression is equivalent to $|-17| + |11| + |-2|$?

    A $17 + 11 + 2$

    B $17 + 11 - 2$

    C $-17 + 11 - 2$

    D $-17 + 11 + 2$

25 Federika spends $60 for two DVDs and a CD. The CD costs $12. The cost of the CD is what percent of the money spent on the DVDs and CD?

    A 5%

    B 10%

    C 15%

    D 20%

26 A flower bed is planted in the shape of a triangle. It has a base of 15 feet and a height of 13 feet. What is the area of the flower bed?

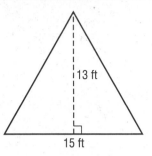

13 ft

15 ft

A 170 square feet

B 97.5 square feet

C 195 square feet

D 225 square feet

27 Which number does *K* represent on the number line?

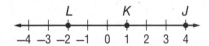

A −2

B 0

C 1

D 4

28 Identify the property shown by 24 × (75 × 12) = 24 × (12 × 75).

A Associative Property of Multiplication

B Commutative Property of Multiplication

C Distributive Property of Multiplication over Addition

D Associative Property of Addition

29 Coach Rodriguez needs to buy water bottles for her softball team. Which unit of measure should she not look for?

A milliliters

B quarts

C pints

D liters

30 Which expression below would you use to find the area of a sector of a circle with a radius of 23 inches and a central angle of 78°?

A $\frac{13}{60} \times 3.14 \times 23 \times 23$

B $\frac{78}{360} \times 3.14 \times 23 \times 2$

C $\frac{13}{60} \times 23 \times 23$

D $\frac{26}{120} \times 3.14 \times 23$

31 Kimora wants to buy a car that costs $5^2 \times 10^3$. How much is the price of the car?

A $1,010

B $1,025

C $10,000

D $25,000

32 Rafiq had a budget of $609 to spend on new clothes for school. He wants to spend the same amount at seven different stores. How much can he spend at each store?

A $79 per store

B $87 per store

C $92 per store

D $96 per store

33 Evaluate the expression $12 \div x - 4$ for $x = 3$.

A 0

B 11

C 32

D 40

Average Monthly Temperature

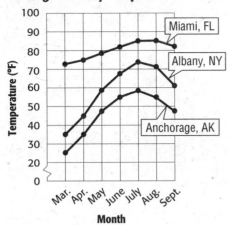

Source: *The World Almanac*

34 How much colder is Anchorage than Miami in July?

A 12°

B 16°

C 27°

D 45°

35 What do you think is the average temperature for Albany in October?

A about 50°

B about 40°

C about 35°

D about 20°

36 The school library has 35 biology books, 17 chemistry books, and 33 physics books. What is the ratio of chemistry books to the number of books in the library written in simplest form?

A 1 to 5

B 85 to 17

C 5 to 1

D 17 to 68

37 In a survey of sixth-graders, 53% said their favorite subject was math. There are 87 sixth-graders in the school. Approximately how many sixth-graders said that math was their favorite subject?

A 10 students

B 45 students

C 50 students

D 70 students

38 Which rectangular prism has a volume of 48 cubic yards?

A
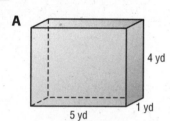
4 yd
1 yd
5 yd

C
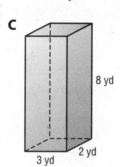
8 yd
2 yd
3 yd

B
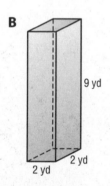
9 yd
2 yd
2 yd

D
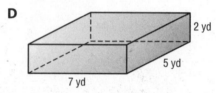
2 yd
5 yd
7 yd

39 Juan bought a bottle of juice that contained 1.25 liters of juice. How many milliliters of juice are in the bottle?

A 12.5 milliliters

B 125 milliliters

C 1,250 milliliters

D 12,500 milliliters

40 Janine needs to write a mathematical sentence that will show the Associative Property of Multiplication. Which sentence should she write?

A $75 \times 1 = 75$

B $88 \times 0 = 0$

C $(4 \times 6) \times 9 = 4 \times (6 \times 9)$

D $69 + 0 = 69$

41 Which is a verbal translation of the algebraic expression $4n + 23$?

A four times a number less 23

B one-fourth of a number less 23

C the sum of a number multiplied by four and 23

D four plus a number plus 23

42 What is the area of the parallelogram shown?

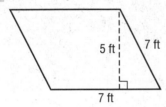

5 ft   7 ft

7 ft

A 25 square feet

B 35 square feet

C 49 square feet

D 72 square feet

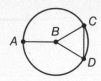

43 Which of the following is not a radius?

   A $\overline{BC}$

   B $\overline{BD}$

   C $\overline{AB}$

   D $\overline{DC}$

44 Which of the following is not a central angle?

   A $\angle ABC$

   B $\angle CBD$

   C $\angle DBA$

   D $\angle BDC$

45 Rina was using some felt to make a border around a picture frame. She used $\frac{1}{3}$ of $\frac{5}{6}$ yard of felt for the border. How much felt did she use?

   A $\frac{1}{5}$ yard

   B $\frac{1}{3}$ yard

   C $\frac{5}{18}$ yard

   D $\frac{5}{6}$ yard

46 There are 35 sixth graders in Mr. Rodriguez's class. In a class poll, 20% said their favorite food was pizza. How many students said their favorite food was pizza?

A 3 students

B 5 students

C 7 students

D 15 students

47 A carton holds 1,000 milliliters of buttermilk. How many liters of buttermilk is this?

A 1

B 10

C 100

D 1,000

48 Nirvelli is going to walk once around a circular walking path in the park.

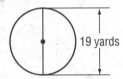
19 yards

Which range of values best describes the circumference of the walking path?

A between 5 and 10 yards

B between 30 and 40 yards

C between 30 and 80 yards

D between 100 and 120 yards

49 Brianna's puppy grew $6\frac{1}{2}$ inches in $3\frac{1}{4}$ months. What was the average growth per month?

A $1\frac{1}{4}$ inches

B 2 inches

C $9\frac{3}{4}$ inches

D $21\frac{1}{8}$ inches

50 Sean and Adriana are making posters for the school pep rally. Sean made $\frac{4}{7}$ of the posters, and Adriana made $\frac{1}{4}$ of them. What fraction of the posters did Sean and Adriana make?

A $\frac{3}{8}$

B $\frac{5}{7}$

C $\frac{23}{28}$

D $\frac{25}{28}$

51 What is the circumference of a circle with a diameter of 15 centimeters? Use 3.14 for π.

A 23.5 centimeters

B 47.1 centimeters

C 94.2 centimeters

D 188.4 centimeters

52 What is the area of the polygon?

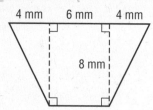

A 20 square millimeters

B 45 square millimeters

C 80 square millimeters

D 160 square millimeters

53 Emma answered $\frac{17}{20}$ of the questions on her last math test correctly. What percent of the questions did she answer correctly?

A 10%

B 49%

C 80%

D 85%

54 Ranajit bought $2\frac{1}{6}$ pounds of raisins and $3\frac{5}{8}$ pounds of peanuts to make a party snack mix. How many more pounds of peanuts did he buy?

A $5\frac{13}{24}$

B $5\frac{19}{24}$

C $2\frac{1}{2}$

D $1\frac{11}{24}$

55 Triangle *MNO* is similar to triangle *PQR*. What is the missing measure *y*?

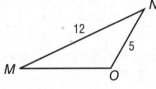

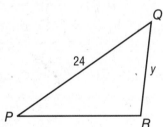

A 2.5

B 10

C 12

D 24

56 A soccer player has a 1-gallon bottle of water. How many pints of water does the soccer player have?

A 1

B 4

C 8

D 24

57 The Anand family is building a deck in their backyard. The deck is a square with sides that measure 11 feet. What is the area of the deck?

A 22 square feet

B 112 square feet

C 120 square feet

D 121 square feet

58 Ari buys a juice box that costs $2 and 3 boxes of crackers that cost $4. Which expression could be used to find the amount of money that Ari spends?

A $2 + 3 \times 4$

B $2 \times 3 + 4$

C $2 + 3 + 4$

D $2 \times 4 + 3$

59 At soccer practice, Nimah made $\frac{9}{16}$ of her penalty kicks. Which decimal is equivalent to $\frac{9}{16}$?

A 0.25

B 0.3333....

C 0.5625

D 0.75

60 Maurice needs $4\frac{5}{16}$ cups of water and $1\frac{1}{4}$ cups of ammonia to make a cleaning solution. How much solution will Maurice make?

A $3\frac{9}{16}$

B $5\frac{9}{16}$

C $3\frac{6}{64}$

D $5\frac{3}{4}$

61 The Brady family needs to put a fence around their circular pool. The pool has a diameter of 25 feet. How many feet of fencing are needed? Use the formula for the circumference of the circle, $C = \pi d$, where d is the diameter. Let $\pi = 3.14$.

A 25 feet

B 46.10 feet

C 78.50 feet

D 157 feet

62 Simplify the expression $7^2 \times 5^1$.

A 19

B 70

C 245

D 350

PART 2

63 Sierra is planning to be the disc jockey for a party. She has made a table showing the lengths of some of the songs she plans to play as a set.

Song	Length (minutes)
1	$4\frac{1}{12}$
2	$3\frac{2}{3}$
3	$5\frac{5}{12}$
4	$6\frac{1}{2}$

Part A

What is the total length in minutes for the four songs? Write your answer in simplest form.

Show your work.

Answer _____

Part B

Sierra wants the set to be no more than 25 minutes long. She has another song she wants to include that is $2\frac{11}{12}$ minutes long. Can she include a sixth song that is $3\frac{1}{6}$ minutes long as well? Explain.

Show your work.

Answer _____

64 Jason built a tower using centimeter cubes. It has a volume of 24 cubic centimeters.

Part A

He wants to make the tower taller, but use the same number of cubes. Change the measures of Jason's tower to fix this problem.

Show your work.

Answer _____

Part B

How can you verify that your model still has a volume of 24 cubic centimeters?

Show your work.

Answer _____

65 Carolina is making three different aprons for a craft fair. She plans to use lace trim on all 3 aprons, but she needs a different amount for each apron.

Apron 1: $\frac{3}{4}$ yard of material

Apron 2: $\frac{1}{2}$ yard of material

Apron 3: $\frac{5}{8}$ yard of material

Part A

If Carolina uses the same color lace for all three aprons, how much lace does she need in all? Write your answer in simplest form.

Show your work.

Answer _____

Part B

Carolina may decide to use a different color lace for apron 3 than for aprons 1 and 2. How much more lace would she need for aprons 1 and 2 than for apron 3? Write your answer in simplest form.

Show your work.

Answer _____

66 A cereal company is promoting its new cereal by placing a small plastic replica of its bear mascot in each box. There are 5 possible colors for the mascot. They are placing more of some colors than of others. If a consumer collects all 5 colors, he or she can trade them in for a $100 gift certificate.

Part A

Complete the table by filling in the missing fractions, decimals, and percents. Write fractions in simplest form.

Show your work.

Plastic Bear Mascots			
Mascot Color	**Fraction**	**Decimal**	**Percent**
Red			45%
Yellow	$\frac{7}{20}$		
Black	$\frac{7}{50}$		
Silver			4%
Gold		0.02	

Part B

Suppose the cereal company has given away 75% of the gift certificates. What percent of the gift certificates has the company not given away? What are the fraction and decimal equivalents of the gift certificates not given away?

Show your work.

Answer _____

67 In 5 seconds, light travels 1,498,962,290 meters.

Part A

Write the number of meters in word form.

Show your work.

Answer _____

_____

Part B

Write the number of meters in expanded form.

Show your work.

Answer _____

_____

68 Ryan took a history test with 25 questions. 60% of the questions were multiple choice.

Part A

How many questions were multiple choice?

Show your work.

Answer _____

Part B

If 8% of the questions are essay questions, how many questions are essay questions?

Show your work.

Answer _____

69 Mr. Singh used a one-year installment plan to buy a computer. On the installment plan, the computer cost $2,400 plus 6% simple interest. Use the formula for simple interest $I = p \times r \times t$.

Part A

What was the amount of simple interest that Mr. Singh paid to buy the computer on the installment plan?

Show your work.

Answer _____

Part B

Mr. Singh made 12 equal monthly payments. What was the amount that he paid each month?

Show your work.

Answer _____

70 A rectangular wooden table has a triangular inlay of a lighter color of wood. Both the base and the height of the inlay measure 2 feet.

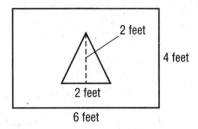

Part A

What is the area of the inlay?

Show your work.

Answer _____

Part B

What is the area of the table that is not part of the inlay?

Show your work.

Answer _____

71 The length of a rectangular swimming pool is 10 feet more than the width.

Part A

Write an algebraic expression for the area of the swimming pool. Indicate what the variable in the expression represents in your work.

Show your work.

Answer _____

Part B

If the length of the swimming pool is 32 feet, what is the area of the swimming pool?

Show your work.

Answer _____

72 The circular section of the arena where circus acts perform is called a ring. The diameter of a circus ring is 42 feet. What is its circumference? Use 3.14 for π.

Part A

Show your work.

Answer _____

Part B

What is the area within the circus ring?

Show your work.

Answer _____

73 Travis wrote 3×27 on the board to show how he uses properties to do mental math. Underneath it, he wrote $3 \times (20 + 7) = \underline{\hspace{2cm}}$.

Part A

What property did Travis use? How do you know?

Show your work.

Answer _____

_____

Part B

Fill in the blank to complete the property he was using.

$3 \times (20 + 7) = \underline{\hspace{2cm}}$

Show your work.

Answer _____

74 A developer has a 15-acre parcel of land. He estimates he needs at least $\frac{3}{5}$-acre for each house he wants to build.

Part A

Explain how you can find the maximum number of houses that the developer could build on the parcel of land. Then find the number of houses.

Show your work.

_____

_____

Answer _____

Part B

The developer decides to set aside $\frac{4}{5}$-acre for a park. If $\frac{3}{8}$ of the park is used for a community garden, what fraction of an acre will be community garden?

Show your work.

Answer _____

75 You can save 10% by buying a $32 jacket while it is on sale.

Part A

Approximately how much money will you save by buying the jacket on sale?
Show your work.

Answer _____

Part B

If you have $25 saved, will you have enough money to buy the jacket? Explain.
Show your work.

Answer _____

76 Mr. Tran bought two types of juice to serve at an after school meeting.
He paid $3.59 for 1,250 milliliters of tangerine juice.
He paid $5.29 for a 2.5-liter bottle of apple juice.

Part A

How many liters of tangerine juice did Mr. Tran buy?

Show your work.

Answer _____

Part B

How many milliliters of apple juice did Mr. Tran buy?

Show your work.

Answer _____

Part C

Which type of juice did Mr. Tran buy more of?

Show your work.

Answer _____

77 Chef Roberts needs to make a large batch of his famous Nutty Granola for a Celebrity Breakfast. His normal recipe includes $10\frac{1}{2}$ cups of oats and $1\frac{3}{4}$ cups of sunflower seeds.

Part A

To make the large batch of granola, Chef Roberts makes $2\frac{1}{2}$ times his normal recipe. How many cups of oats and of sunflower seeds would he use in the large batch?

Show your work.

Answer _____

Part B

To make the large batch of granola, Chef Roberts uses $6\frac{1}{4}$ cups of almonds. How many cups of almonds does he use in his normal recipe?

Show your work.

Answer _____

78 Use the graph below to answer parts A and B.

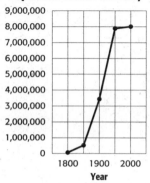

Part A

Use the data in the graph to describe the pattern or trend of the population of New York City.

Show your work.

Answer _____

_____

Part B

What do you predict the population to be in 2050?

Show your work.

Answer _____

79 $125 + 6^2 \times (3 - 1)$

Part A

When evaluating this expression, which operation should you do first? Explain.

Show your work.

Answer _____

Part B

Find the value of the expression.

Show your work.

Answer _____

80 Tiffany received $135 for her birthday. She wants to buy a flute that costs $450.

Part A

What percent of the flute's price did she receive for her birthday?

Show your work.

Answer _____

Part B

Tiffany has earned $189 babysitting. If she combines the babysitting money and the birthday money, what percent of the cost of the flute will she have?

Show your work.

Answer _____

81 Write down the names of seven states. Count the number of letters in each state name and record the data. For example, New York has 7 letters in its name.

Part A

What is the mean of the data?

Show your work.

Answer _____

Part B

What is the median of the data?

Show your work.

Answer _____

82 Miguel's class is doing a papier-mâché art project. He is making the papier-mâché paste for the whole class. The recipe calls for $2\frac{1}{2}$ cups of water, $1\frac{1}{4}$ cups of flour, and 2 tablespoons of salt. How many pints of water will he need to make 4 times the given recipe?

Show your work.

Answer _____

83 Draw a circle. Label the center C. Draw a central angle and label it $\angle ACB$. Draw a diameter $\overline{EF}$.

Part A

Show your work.

Answer _____

Part B

If the measure of $\overline{EC}$ is 9 centimeters, how long is $\overline{EF}$?

Show your work.

Answer _____

84 Mrs. Summers is keeping a record of how far she walks each day.

Day	Distance walked (in miles)
Monday	$1\frac{1}{2}$
Tuesday	$\frac{3}{8}$
Wednesday	$1\frac{1}{3}$
Thursday	$\frac{2}{3}$
Friday	$2\frac{1}{4}$
Saturday	$1\frac{5}{6}$

Part A

Plot the distances on the number line below. Label each point. Explain how you plotted the points.

Show your work.

Answer _____

Part B

What is the order of the distances from longest to shortest distance? Explain how you used the number line to order the distances.

Show your work.

Answer _____

85 Mr. Sanchez needs to supply lunches for 24 students. He can buy platters of 6 sandwiches for $15 and packs of 3 juice boxes for $1.95. What is the cost per student for a sandwich and a juice box?

Show your work.

Answer _____

86 Your teacher writes the following on the board.

$$2 \times 2 \times 2 \times 5 \times 5 \times 7 \times 7 \times 7$$

Part A

How would you write this expression using exponents?

Show your work.

Answer _____

Part B

Your teacher writes the following on the board: $2 \times 2 \times 3 \times 3 \times 3 \times 5 \times 7 \times 9 \times 9$. One of your classmates writes the expression using exponents as $2^2 \times 3^2 \times 5 \times 7 \times 9^2$. Is your classmate correct? Explain.

Show your work.

Answer _____

87 Ms. Madigan's garden is in the shape of an irregular pentagon. She raises herbs, strawberries, and pumpkins. Remember that the formula for a triangle is $A = \frac{1}{2}bh$, and the formula for the area of a trapezoid is $A = \frac{1}{2}(b_1 + b_2)h$.

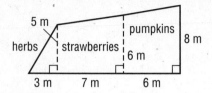

Part A

What is the total area of the garden?

Show your work.

Answer _____

Part B

Is more of the garden pumpkins or strawberries? How much more?

Show your work.

Answer _____

88 Rebecca needs to make punch for a class party. Each punch bowl holds 2 gallons. How many cups of punch will each bowl hold when filled?

Show your work.

Answer _____

89 The Associated Student Council has 80 items to sell in a bake sale. Of the items for sale, 40% are cupcakes.

Part A

How many cupcakes are in the bake sale?

Show your work.

Answer _____

Part B

If 75% of the cupcakes are frosted, how many frosted cupcakes are in the bake sale?

Show your work.

Answer _____

90 Patrick is helping the veterinarian add liquid vitamins and medicines to the feed of animals in the clinic.

Part A

Which unit of measure is Patrick likely to use to measure the vitamins and medicines? Explain.

Explain your answer.

Answer _____

Part B

Patrick finds an eyedropper that measures up to 10 milliliters. Would this be a good measuring tool for him to use?

Explain your answer.

Answer _____

91 Lindsey's class is painting an ocean scene on a rectangular area of the playground. The painting will measure 18 feet by 26 feet when it is completed. She estimates the area of the rectangle to be 260 square feet.

Part A

Is this a reasonable estimate? Explain.

Show your work.

Answer _____

Part B

If a climbing structure in the shape of a rectangular prism 5 feet tall were built above the playground painting, what would be the exact volume of the structure?

Show your work.

Answer _____

92 Marco eats a slice of pizza that is a sector of a circle. The diameter of the pizza is 20 inches.

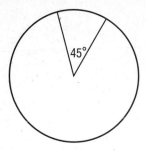

Part A

Find the area of the sector. Use 3.14 for π. Round your answer to nearest hundredth.
Show your work.

Answer _____

Part B

What happens to the area of the sector if the central angle is tripled?
Show your work.

Answer _____

93 △DEF : △RTS.

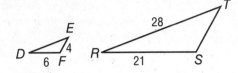

Part A

What is the length of $\overline{DE}$?

Show your work.

Answer _____

Part B

What is the length of $\overline{ST}$?

Show your work.

Answer _____

Glossary

A

absolute value (94) The distance between a number and zero on a number line. The absolute value of both −5 and 5 is the same, since both are the same distance from 0: $|5| = 5$, $|-5| = 5$.

algebraic expression (1) An expression that contains operations with variables and numbers.

arc (187) A part of a circle.

Associative Properties of Addition and Multiplication (63) These properties state that the grouping of the addends or factors does not change the sum or products.

B

bar graph (230) A graph that compares data by using bars of different lengths or heights to show values.

base (85) In a percent problem, the original or whole amount that the part is being compared to. (126) In a power, the number used as a factor.

C

capacity (196) The amount that a container can hold.

central angle (179) An angle whose vertex is the center of the circle.

chord (179) A line segment that connects two points on a circle.

circumference (183) The distance, also known as the length, around a circle.

Commutative Properties of Addition and Multiplication (63) These properties state that the order in which two numbers are added or multiplied does not change the sum or product.

congruent (157) Figures that have the same size and shape.

coordinate plane (15) A plane formed when two number lines (called axes) intersect at right angles at their zero points; also called the coordinate system.

corresponding sides (157) The sides of similar triangles that match.

cup (c) (201) A customary unit that is used to measure capacity.

D

diameter (179) A chord that passes through the center of a circle or the length of that chord.

digit (58) A symbol used to write a number. The ten digits are 0, 1, 2, 3, 4, 5, 6, 7, 8, 9.

Distributive Property of Multiplication over Addition (63) This property states that to multiply a sum by a number, you can multiply each addend by the same number and add the products.

E

equation (6) A mathematical statement with an equals sign, =, indicating that the left side of the equals sign has the same value as the right side.

equivalent ratios (70) Ratios that can be represented by equivalent fractions.

estimate (135, 217) An approximate amount, that is, a number close to an exact value. An estimate indicates about how much.

evaluate (1) To find the value of an algebraic expression.

event (34) A set of outcomes in a probability experiment.

expanded form/expanded notation (58) A number shown as a sum that shows the value of each digit.

exponent (126) The number in a power that shows how many times the base is used as a factor.

extremes (75) In a proportion, the numerator of the first fraction and the denominator of the second fraction.

F

formula (148) An equation that describes a relationship between two or more quantities.

G

gallon (gal) (201) A customary unit of capacity equal to four quarts.

I

Identity Properties of Addition and Multiplication (63) Properties that state that if you add a number to 0, the sum is the same as the given number, and if you multiply a number by 1, the product is the same as the given number.

improper fraction (114) A fraction that has a numerator that is greater than or equal to the denominator.

inverse operations (6) Operations that undo each other. Addition and subtraction are inverse operations. Multiplication and division are inverse operations.

Inverse Property of Addition (63) This property states that when a number is subtracted from itself, the result is 0.

Inverse Property of Multiplication (63) This property states then when a number is divided by itself or multiplied by its reciprocal, the result is 1.

L

Least Common Denominator (LCD) (99) The least common multiple of the denominators of two or more fractions, used as a denominator.

line graph (230) A graph that uses points connected by line segments to represent changes in data over a period of time.

liter (L) (206) The basic unit of capacity in the metric system. One liter equals one thousand milliliters.

M

mean (226) The quotient found by adding the numbers in the set of data and dividing this sum by the number of addends.

means (75) In a proportion, the denominator of the first fraction and the numerator of the second fraction.

median (226) The middle number in a set of data when it is arranged in numerical order. If the data set has an even number, the median is the mean of the two middle numbers.

milliliter (mL) (206) One of the most common metric units of capacity. One milliliter equals one-thousandth of a liter.

mixed number (109) The sum of a whole number and a fraction. Example: $3\frac{1}{3}$

mode (226) The number(s) or item(s) that occur most often in a set of data. A set can have more than one mode.

multiplicative inverse (104) The number that, when multiplied by a given number, results in a product of one.

O

order of operations (130) The order in which operations should be performed when evaluating expressions.

ordered pair (15) A pair of numbers that are the coordinates of a point in a coordinate plane in this order (horizontal coordinate, vertical coordinate).

origin (15) The point (0, 0) on a coordinate plane where the vertical axis meets the horizontal axis.

outcome (34) A possible result of an experiment.

P

parallelogram (20) A quadrilateral in which each pair of opposite sides is parallel and equal in length.

part (85) The amount being compared to the whole amount in a percent problem.

percent (80) A ratio of a part of a whole divided into hundredths to 100.

perimeter (25) The distance around a shape or region.

period (58) A three-digit group of numbers from a place-value chart.

pictograph (230) A graph that compares data by using picture symbols.

pint (pt) (201) A customary unit of capacity equal to two cups.

precision (213) An indication of the accuracy of a measurement; depends on the units of measure you use. The smaller the unit of measure you use, the greater the precision.

polygon (167) A simple closed plane figure formed by three or more line segments.

power (126) A number that can be expressed using an exponent.

probability (38) The chance that some event will occur.

proportion (70) An equation stating that two ratios or rates are equivalent.

Q

quart (qt) (201) A customary unit of capacity equal to two pints.

R

radius (179) A line segment that connects the center of a circle to a point on the circle or the length of that segment.

range (226) The difference between the greatest number and the least number in a set of data.

rate (70) A ratio that compares two quantities with different kinds of units.

ratio (70) A comparison of two quantities by division.

rational number (94) Any number that can be written as a fraction.

reciprocal (104) The multiplicative inverse of the number.

rectangle (20) A quadrilateral with four right angles; opposite sides are equal and parallel.

rectangular prism (172) A solid figure that has two parallel and congruent bases that are rectangles.

regular polygon (167) A polygon that has all sides congruent and all angles congruent.

repeating decimal (119) A decimal in which a pattern of one or more digits is repeated indefinitely.

rhombus (162) A parallelogram with four congruent sides.

S

sample space (38) The set of all possible outcomes in a probability experiment.

sector (187) Part of a circle bounded by two radii and an arc.

similar triangles (157) Triangles that have the same shape but not necessarily the same size.

simplest form of a fraction (99) The form of a fraction when the numerator and denominater have no common factor greater than 1.

solution (6) The value that makes an equation true.

square (20) A rectangle with four congruent sides.

standard form/standard notation (58) The usual way of writing a number that shows only its digits, no words.

T

terminating decimal (119) A decimal that ends.

trapezoid (162) A quadrilateral with exactly one pair of parallel sides.

triangle (20) A polygon with three sides and three angles.

U

unlike fractions (99) Fractions with different denominators.

V

variable (1) A letter or symbol used to represent an unknown quantity.

volume (172) The number of cube units needed to fill the space occupied by a solid figure.

X

x-axis (15) The horizontal axis in a coordinate plane.

x-coordinate (15) The first number of an ordered pair.

Y

y-axis (15) The vertical axis in a coordinate plane.

y-coordinate (15) The second number of an ordered pair.

Z

Zero Property of Multiplication (63) This property states that any number multiplied by zero is zero.

Index

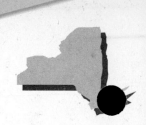

P

Q

R

S